Glencoe

Algebra 1

Integration
Applications
Connections

Enrichment Masters

GLENCOE

McGraw-Hill

New York, New York   Columbus, Ohio   Mission Hills, California   Peoria, Illinois

Glencoe/McGraw-Hill

A Division of The McGraw·Hill Companies

Send all inquiries to:
Glencoe/McGraw-Hill
936 Eastwind Drive
Westerville, OH 43081

ISBN: 0-02-824874-0

Algebra 1
Enrichment Masters

2 3 4 5 6 7 8 9 10   066   03 02 01 00 99 98 97

Contents

1–1

Enrichment

The Four Digits Problem

One well-known problem in mathematics is to write expressions for consecutive numbers from 1 upward as far as possible. On this page, you will use the digits 1, 2, 3, and 4. Each digit is used only once. You can use addition, subtraction, multiplication (not division), exponents, and parentheses in any way you wish. Also, you can use two digits to make one number, as in 12 or 34.

Express each number as a combination of the digits 1, 2, 3, and 4.

$1 = (3 \times 1) - (4 - 2)$

$2 = $ _____

$3 = $ _____

$4 = $ _____

$5 = $ _____

$6 = $ _____

$7 = $ _____

$8 = $ _____

$9 = $ _____

$10 = $ _____

$11 = $ _____

$12 = $ _____

$13 = $ _____

$14 = $ _____

$15 = $ _____

$16 = $ _____

$17 = $ _____

$18 = $ _____

$19 = 3(2 + 4) + 1$

$20 = $ _____

$21 = $ _____

$22 = $ _____

$23 = 31 - (4 \times 2)$

$24 = $ _____

$25 = $ _____

$26 = $ _____

$27 = $ _____

$28 = $ _____

$29 = $ _____

$30 = $ _____

$31 = $ _____

$32 = $ _____

$33 = $ _____

$34 = $ _____

$35 = 2^{(4+1)} + 3$

$36 = $ _____

$37 = $ _____

$38 = $ _____

$39 = $ _____

$40 = $ _____

$41 = $ _____

$42 = $ _____

$43 = 42 + 1^3$

$44 = $ _____

$45 = $ _____

$46 = $ _____

$47 = $ _____

$48 = $ _____

$49 = $ _____

$50 = $ _____

Does a calculator help in solving these types of puzzles? Give reasons for your opinion.

_____

_____

_____

Algebra 1

Enrichment

The Four Digits Problem

One well-known problem in mathematics is to write expressions for consecutive numbers from 1 upward as far as possible. On this page, you will use the digits 1, 2, 3, and 4. Each digit is used only once. You can use addition, subtraction, multiplication (not division), exponents, and parentheses in any way you wish. Also, you can use two digits to make one number, as in 12 or 34.

Answers will vary. Sample answers are given.

Express each number as a combination of the digits 1, 2, 3, and 4.

$1 = (3 \times 1) - (4 - 2)$

$2 = (4 - 3) + (2 - 1)$

$3 = (4 - 3) + (2 \times 1)$

$4 = (4 - 2) + (3 - 1)$

$5 = (4 - 2) + (3 \times 1)$

$6 = 4 + 3 + 1 - 2$

$7 = 3(4 - 1) - 2$

$8 = 4 + 3 + 2 - 1$

$9 = 4 + 2 + (3 \times 1)$

$10 = 4 + 3 + 2 + 1$

$11 = (4 \times 3) - (2 - 1)$

$12 = (4 \times 3) \times (2 - 1)$

$13 = (4 \times 3) + (2 - 1)$

$14 = (4 \times 3) + (2 \times 1)$

$15 = 2(3 + 4) + 1$

$16 = (4 \times 2) \times (3 - 1)$

$17 = 3(2 + 4) - 1$

$18 = (2 \times 3) \times (4 - 1)$

$19 = 3(2 + 4) + 1$

$20 = 21 - (4 - 3)$

$21 = (4 + 3) \times (2 + 1)$

$22 = 21 + (4 - 3)$

$23 = 31 - (4 \times 2)$

$24 = (2 + 4) \times (3 + 1)$

$25 = (2 + 3) \times (4 + 1)$

$26 = 24 + (3 - 1)$

$27 = 3^2 \times (4 - 1)$

$28 = 21 + 3 + 4$

$29 = 2^{(4+1)} - 3$

$30 = (2 \times 3) \times (4 + 1)$

$31 = 34 - (2 + 1)$

$32 = 4^2 \times (3 - 1)$

$33 = 21 + (3 \times 4)$

$34 = 2 \times (14 + 3)$

$35 = 2^{(4+1)} + 3$

$36 = 34 + (2 \times 1)$

$37 = 31 + 2 + 4$

$38 = 42 - (3 + 1)$

$39 = 42 - (3 \times 1)$

$40 = 41 - (3 - 2)$

$41 = 43 - (2 \times 1)$

$42 = 43 - (2 - 1)$

$43 = 42 + 1^3$

$44 = 43 + (2 - 1)$

$45 = 43 + (2 \times 1)$

$46 = 43 + (2 + 1)$

$47 = 31 + 4^2$

$48 = 4^2 \times (3 \times 1)$

$49 = 41 + 2^3$

$50 = 41 + 3^2$

Does a calculator help in solving these types of puzzles? Give reasons for your opinion.

Answers will vary. _____

_____

_____

Enrichment

The Tower of Hanoi

The Tower of Hanoi puzzle has three pegs, with a stack of disks on peg a. The object is to move all of the disks to another peg. You may move only one disk at a time. Also, a larger disk may never be put on top of a smaller disk.

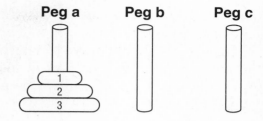

A chart has been started to record your moves as you solve the puzzle.

Another way to record the moves is to use letters. For example, the first two steps in the chart can be recorded as 1c, 2b. This shows that disk 1 is moved to peg c, and then disk 2 is moved to peg b.

Solve each problem.

1. Finish the chart to solve the Tower of Hanoi puzzle for three disks.

2. Record your solution using letters.

3. On a separate sheet of paper, solve the puzzle for four disks. Record your solution.

4. Solve the puzzle for five disks. Record your solution.

5. If you start with an odd number of disks and you want to end with the stack on peg c, what should be your first move?

6. If you start with an even number of disks and you want to end with the stack on peg b, what should be your first move?

Peg a	Peg b	Peg c
1 2 3		
2 3		1
3	2	1

2

Algebra 1

NAME_____ DATE _____

Enrichment

The Tower of Hanoi

The Tower of Hanoi puzzle has three pegs, with a stack of disks on peg a. The object is to move all of the disks to another peg. You may move only one disk at a time. Also, a larger disk may never be put on top of a smaller disk.

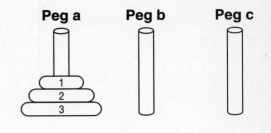

A chart has been started to record your moves as you solve the puzzle.

Another way to record the moves is to use letters. For example, the first two steps in the chart can be recorded as 1c, 2b. This shows that disk 1 is moved to peg c, and then disk 2 is moved to peg b.

Solve each problem.

1. Finish the chart to solve the Tower of Hanoi puzzle for three disks.

2. Record your solution using letters.
   1c, 2b, 1b, 3c, 1a, 2c, 1c

3. On a separate sheet of paper, solve the puzzle for four disks. Record your solution.
   **1c, 2b, 1b, 3c, 1a, 2c, 1c,
   4b, 1b, 2a, 1a, 3b, 1c, 2b, 1b**

4. Solve the puzzle for five disks. Record your solution.
   **1c, 2b, 1b, 3c, 1a, 2c, 1c, 4b, 1b, 2a, 1a, 3b,
   1c, 2b, 1b, 5c, 1a, 2c, 1c, 3a, 1b, 2a, 1a, 4c,
   1c, 2b, 1b, 3c, 1a, 2c, 1c**

5. If you start with an odd number of disks and you want to end with the stack on peg c, what should be your first move?
   1c

6. If you start with an even number of disks and you want to end with the stack on peg b, what should be your first move?
   1c

Peg a	Peg b	Peg c
1 2 3		
2 3		1
3	2	1
3	1 2	
	1 2	3
1	2	3
1		2 3
		1 2 3

NAME_____ DATE _____

Enrichment

Puzzling Primes

A *prime number* has only two factors, itself and 1. The number 6 is not prime because it has 2 and 3 as factors; 5 and 7 are prime. The number 1 is not considered to be prime.

1. Use a calculator to help you find the 25 prime numbers less than 100.

_____

_____

Prime numbers have interested mathematicians for centuries. They have tried to find expressions that will give all the prime numbers, or only prime numbers. In the 1700s, Euler discovered that the expression $x^2 + x + 41$ will yield prime numbers for values of x from 0 through 39.

2. Find the prime numbers generated by Euler's formula for x from 0 through 7.

_____

3. Show that the expression $x^2 + x + 31$ will not give prime numbers for very many values of x.

_____

4. Find the largest prime number generated by Euler's formula. _____

Goldbach's Conjecture is that every nonzero even number greater than 2 can be written as the sum of two primes. No one has ever proved that this is always true. No one has disproved it, either.

5. Show that Goldbach's Conjecture is true for the first 5 even numbers greater than 2.

_____

6. Give a way that someone could disprove Goldbach's Conjecture.

_____

_____

Algebra 1

Enrichment

Puzzling Primes

A *prime number* has only two factors, itself and 1. The number 6 is not prime because it has 2 and 3 as factors; 5 and 7 are prime. The number 1 is not considered to be prime.

1. Use a calculator to help you find the 25 prime numbers less than 100.

2, 3, 5, 7, 11, 13, 17, 19, 23, 29, 31, 37 41, 43, 47, 53, 59, 61,

67, 71, 73, 79, 83, 89, 97

Prime numbers have interested mathematicians for centuries. They have tried to find expressions that will give all the prime numbers, or only prime numbers. In the 1700s, Euler discovered that the expression $x^2 + x + 41$ will yield prime numbers for values of x from 0 through 39.

2. Find the prime numbers generated by Euler's formula for x from 0 through 7.

41, 43, 47, 53, 61, 71, 83, 97

3. Show that the expression $x^2 + x + 31$ will not give prime numbers for very many values of x.

It works for x = 0, 2, 3, 5, and 6 but not for x = 1, 4, and 7.

4. Find the largest prime number generated by Euler's formula. _____**1601**_____

Goldbach's Conjecture is that every nonzero even number greater than 2 can be written as the sum of two primes. No one has ever proved that this is always true. No one has disproved it, either.

5. Show that Goldbach's Conjecture is true for the first 5 even numbers greater than 2.

$4 = 2 + 2$, $6 = 3 + 3$, $8 = 3 + 5$, $10 = 3 + 7$, $12 = 5 + 7$

6. Give a way that someone could disprove Goldbach's Conjecture.

Find an even number that cannot be written as the sum of

two primes.

NAME_____ DATE_____

Enrichment

Latin Squares

In designing a statistical experiment, it is important to try to randomize the variables. For example, suppose 4 different motor oils are being compared to see which give the best gasoline mileage. An experimenter might then choose 4 different drivers and four different cars. To test-drive all the possible combinations, the experimenter would need 64 test-drives.

To reduce the number of test drives, a statistician might use an arrangement called a **Latin Square**.

For this example, the four motor oils are labeled A, B, C, and D and are arranged as shown. Each oil must appear exactly one time in each row and column of the square.

The drivers are labeled D(1), D(2), D(3), and D(4); the cars are labeled C(1), C(2), C(3), and C(4).

	D(1)	D(2)	D(3)	D(4)
C(1)	A	B	C	D
C(2)	B	A	D	C
C(3)	C	D	A	B
C(4)	D	C	B	A

Now, the number of test-drives is just 16, one for each cell of the Latin Square.

Create two 4-by-4 Latin Squares that are different from the example.

1.

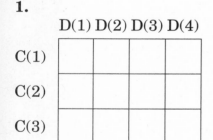

2.

Make three different 3-by-3 Latin Squares.

3.

4.

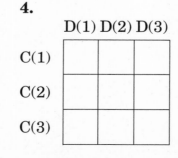

5.

4

Enrichment

Latin Squares

In designing a statistical experiment, it is important to try to
randomize the variables. For example, suppose 4 different
motor oils are being compared to see which give the best
gasoline mileage. An experimenter might then choose 4
different drivers and four different cars. To test-drive all the
possible combinations, the experimenter would need 64
test-drives.

To reduce the number of test drives, a statistician
might use an arrangement called a **Latin Square**.

For this example, the four motor oils are labeled A,
B, C, and D and are arranged as shown. Each oil
must appear exactly one time in each row and
column of the square.

The drivers are labeled D(1), D(2), D(3), and D(4);
the cars are labeled C(1), C(2), C(3), and C(4).

Now, the number of test-drives is just 16, one for
each cell of the Latin Square.

	D(1)	D(2)	D(3)	D(4)
C(1)	A	B	C	D
C(2)	B	A	D	C
C(3)	C	D	A	B
C(4)	D	C	B	A

**Create two 4-by-4 Latin Squares that are different from the
example. Answers will vary. Sample answers are given.**

1.

	D(1)	D(2)	D(3)	D(4)
C(1)	B	C	A	D
C(2)	D	A	C	B
C(3)	C	D	B	A
C(4)	A	B	D	C

2.

	D(1)	D(2)	D(3)	D(4)
C(1)	D	C	B	A
C(2)	A	B	C	D
C(3)	B	D	A	C
C(4)	C	A	D	B

Make three different 3-by-3 Latin Squares.

3.

	D(1)	D(2)	D(3)
C(1)	A	B	C
C(2)	B	C	A
C(3)	C	A	B

4.

	D(1)	D(2)	D(3)
C(1)	A	C	B
C(2)	C	B	A
C(3)	B	A	C

5.

	D(1)	D(2)	D(3)
C(1)	B	C	A
C(2)	C	A	B
C(3)	A	B	C

1–5

Enrichment

Solution Sets

Consider the following open sentence.

It is the tallest building in the world.

You know that a replacement for the variable *It* must be found in order to determine if the sentence is true or false. If *It* is replaced by either the Empire State Building or the Sears Tower, the sentence is true.

The set {Empire State Building, Sears Tower} is called the *solution set* of the open sentence given above. This set includes all replacements for the variable that make the sentence true.

Write the solution set of each open sentence.

1. It is the name of a state beginning with the letter A.

1. _____

2. It is a primary color.

2. _____

3. Its capital is Harrisburg.

3. _____

4. It is a New England state.

4. _____

5. $x + 4 = 10$

5. _____

6. It is the name of a month that contains the letter r.

6. _____

7. During the 1970s, she was the wife of a U.S. President.

7. _____

8. It is an even number between 1 and 13.

8. _____

9. $31 = 72 - k$

9. _____

10. It is the square of 2, 3, or 4.

10. _____

Write an open sentence for each solution set.

11. {A, E, I, O, U}

11. _____

12. {1, 3, 5, 7, 9}

12. _____

13. {June, July, August}

13. _____

14. {Atlantic, Pacific, Indian, Arctic}

14. _____

NAME_____ DATE _____

Enrichment

Solution Sets

Consider the following open sentence.

It is the tallest building in the world.

You know that a replacement for the variable *It* must be found in order to determine if the sentence is true or false. If *It* is replaced by either the Empire State Building or the Sears Tower, the sentence is true.

The set {Empire State Building, Sears Tower} is called the *solution set* of the open sentence given above. This set includes all replacements for the variable that make the sentence true.

Write the solution set of each open sentence.

1. It is the name of a state beginning with the letter A.

   1. {Alabama, Alaska, Arizona, Arkansas}

2. It is a primary color.

   2. {red, yellow, blue}

3. Its capital is Harrisburg.

   3. {Pennsylvania}

4. It is a New England state.

   4. {Maine, New Hamp., Vermont, Mass., Rhode Is., Conn.}

5. $x + 4 = 10$

   5. {6}

6. It is the name of a month that contains the letter *r*.

   6. {Jan, Feb, Mar, Apr, Sept, Oct, Nov, Dec}

7. During the 1970s, she was the wife of a U.S. President.

   7. {Pat Nixon, Betty Ford, Rosalyn Carter}

8. It is an even number between 1 and 13.

   8. {2, 4, 6, 8, 10, 12}

9. $31 = 72 - k$

   9. {41}

10. It is the square of 2, 3, or 4.

    10. {4, 9, 16}

Write an open sentence for each solution set.

11. {A, E, I, O, U}

    11. It is a vowel.

12. {1, 3, 5, 7, 9}

    12. It is an odd number between 0 and 10.

13. {June, July, August}

    13. It is a summer month.

14. {Atlantic, Pacific, Indian, Arctic}

    14. It is an ocean.

Algebra 1

Enrichment

The Conditional Statement

If p and q represent statements, the compound statement
"if p then q" is called a *conditional*.

symbol: $p \rightarrow q$ read: either "if p then q" or "p only if q"

The statement p is called the *antecedent*, and the statement q is
called the *consequent*.

**For each conditional statement identify the antecedent (A) and
the consequent (C).**

1. If it is nine o'clock, then I am late.

A: _____

C: _____

2. If Karen is home, then we will ask her to come.

A: _____

C: _____

3. The fish will die if we don't feed them.

A: _____

C: _____

4. There will be no school if it snows.

A: _____

C: _____

5. There will be no school only if it snows.

A: _____

C: _____

6. If $y + 2 = 6$ then $y = 4$.

A: _____

C: _____

Enrichment

The Conditional Statement

If p and q represent statements, the compound statement
"if p then q" is called a *conditional*.

symbol: $p \rightarrow q$ read: either "if p then q" or "p only if q"

The statement p is called the *antecedent*, and the statement q is
called the *consequent*.

**For each conditional statement identify the antecedent (A) and
the consequent (C).**

1. If it is nine o'clock, then I am late.

A: It is 9:00.

C: I am late.

2. If Karen is home, then we will ask her to come.

A: Karen is home.

C: We will ask Karen to come.

3. The fish will die if we don't feed them.

A: We don't feed the fish.

C: The fish will die.

4. There will be no school if it snows.

A: It snows, or it is snowing.

C: There will be no school.

5. There will be no school only if it snows.

A: There will be no school.

C: It is snowing.

6. If $y + 2 = 6$ then $y = 4$.

A: $y + 2 = 6$

C: $y = 4$

Enrichment

Closure

A *binary operation* matches two numbers in a set to just one number. Addition is a binary operation on the set of whole numbers. It matches two numbers such as 4 and 5 to a single number, their sum.

If the result of a binary operation is always a member of the original set, the set is said to be *closed* under the operation. For example, the set of whole numbers is not closed under subtraction because $3 - 6$ is not a whole number.

Is each operation binary? Write <u>yes</u> or <u>no</u>.

1. the operation $\hookleftarrow$, where $a \hookleftarrow b$ means to choose the lesser number from a and b

2. the operation $\copyright$, where $a \copyright b$ means to cube the sum of a and b

3. the operation sq, where $sq(a)$ means to square the number a

4. the operation exp, where $exp(a, b)$ means to find the value of a^b

5. the operation $\Uparrow$, where $a \Uparrow b$ means to match a and b to any number greater than either number

6. the operation $\Rightarrow$, where $a \Rightarrow b$ means to round the product of a and b up to the nearest 10

Is each set closed under addition? Write <u>yes</u> or <u>no</u>. If your answer is no, give an example.

7. even numbers

8. odd numbers

9. multiples of 3

10. multiples of 5

11. prime numbers

12. nonprime numbers

Is the set of whole numbers closed under each operation? Write <u>yes</u> or <u>no</u>. If your answer is no, give an example.

13. multiplication: $a \times b$

14. division: $a \div b$

15. exponentation: a^b

16. squaring the sum: $(a + b)^2$

7

Algebra 1

Enrichment

Closure

A *binary operation* matches two numbers in a set to just one number. Addition is a binary operation on the set of whole numbers. It matches two numbers such as 4 and 5 to a single number, their sum.

If the result of a binary operation is always a member of the original set, the set is said to be *closed* under the operation. For example, the set of whole numbers is not closed under subtraction because $3 - 6$ is not a whole number.

Is each operation binary? Write yes or no.

1. the operation ↵, where $a ↵ b$ means to choose the lesser number from a and b **yes**

2. the operation ©, where $a © b$ means to cube the sum of a and b **yes**

3. the operation sq, where $sq(a)$ means to square the number a **no**

4. the operation exp, where $exp(a, b)$ means to find the value of a^b **yes**

5. the operation ⇑, where $a ⇑ b$ means to match a and b to any number greater than either number **no**

6. the operation ⇒, where $a ⇒ b$ means to round the product of a and b up to the nearest 10 **yes**

Is each set closed under addition? Write yes or no. If your answer is no, give an example.

7. even numbers **yes**

8. odd numbers **no; $3 + 7 = 10$**

9. multiples of 3 **yes**

10. multiples of 5 **yes**

11. prime numbers **no; $3 + 5 = 8$**

12. nonprime numbers **no; $22 + 9 = 31$**

Is the set of whole numbers closed under each operation? Write yes or no. If your answer is no, give an example.

13. multiplication: $a \times b$ **yes**

14. division: $a \div b$ **no; $4 \div 3$ is not a whole number**

15. exponentiation: a^b **yes**

16. squaring the sum: $(a + b)^2$ **yes**

Properties of Operations

Let's make up a new operation and denote it by ⊛, so that $a ⊛ b$ means b^a.

$2 ⊛ 3 = 3^2 = 9$

$(1 ⊛ 2) ⊛ 3 = 2^1 ⊛ 3 = 3^2 = 9$

1. What number is represented by $2 ⊛ 3$? _____

2. What number is represented by $3 ⊛ 2$? _____

3. Does the operation ⊛ appear to be commutative? _____

4. What number is represented by $(2 ⊛ 1) ⊛ 3$? _____

5. What number is represented by $2 ⊛ (1 ⊛ 3)$? _____

6. Does the operation ⊛ appear to be associative? _____

Let's make up another operation and denote it by ⊕,
so that $a ⊕ b = (a + 1)(b + 1)$.

$3 ⊕ 2 = (3 + 1)(2 + 1) = 4 \cdot 3 = 12$

$(1 ⊕ 2) ⊕ 3 = (2 \cdot 3) ⊕ 3 = 6 ⊕ 3 = 7 \cdot 4 = 28$

7. What number is represented by $2 ⊕ 3$? _____

8. What number is represented by $3 ⊕ 2$? _____

9. Does the operation ⊕ appear to be commutative? _____

10. What number is represented by $(2 ⊕ 3) ⊕ 4$? _____

11. What number is represented by $2 ⊕ (3 ⊕ 4)$? _____

12. Does the operation ⊕ appear to be associative? _____

13. What number is represented by $1 ⊛ (3 ⊕ 2)$? _____

14. What number is represented by $(1 ⊛ 3) ⊕ (1 ⊛ 2)$? _____

15. Does the operation ⊛ appear to be distributive over the operation ⊕? _____

16. Let's explore these operations a little further. What number is

    represented by $3 ⊛ (4 ⊕ 2)$? _____

17. What number is represented by $(3 ⊛ 4) ⊕ (3 ⊛ 2)$? _____

18. Is the operation ⊛ actually distributive over the operation ⊕? _____

Algebra 1

NAME_____ DATE _____

Enrichment

Properties of Operations

Let's make up a new operation and denote it by $\circledast$, so that $a \circledast b$ means b^a.

$2 \circledast 3 = 3^2 = 9$

$(1 \circledast 2) \circledast 3 = 2^1 \circledast 3 = 3^2 = 9$

1. What number is represented by $2 \circledast 3$? ___$3^2 = 9$___

2. What number is represented by $3 \circledast 2$? ___$2^3 = 8$___

3. Does the operation $\circledast$ appear to be commutative? ___no___

4. What number is represented by $(2 \circledast 1) \circledast 3$? ___3___

5. What number is represented by $2 \circledast (1 \circledast 3)$? ___9___

6. Does the operation $\circledast$ appear to be associative? ___no___

Let's make up another operation and denote it by $\oplus$, so that $a \oplus b = (a + 1)(b + 1)$.

$3 \oplus 2 = (3 + 1)(2 + 1) = 4 \cdot 3 = 12$

$(1 \oplus 2) \oplus 3 = (2 \cdot 3) \oplus 3 = 6 \oplus 3 = 7 \cdot 4 = 28$

7. What number is represented by $2 \oplus 3$? ___12___

8. What number is represented by $3 \oplus 2$? ___12___

9. Does the operation $\oplus$ appear to be commutative? ___yes___

10. What number is represented by $(2 \oplus 3) \oplus 4$? ___65___

11. What number is represented by $2 \oplus (3 \oplus 4)$? ___63___

12. Does the operation $\oplus$ appear to be associative? ___no___

13. What number is represented by $1 \circledast (3 \oplus 2)$? ___12___

14. What number is represented by $(1 \circledast 3) \oplus (1 \circledast 2)$? ___12___

15. Does the operation $\circledast$ appear to be distributive over the operation $\oplus$? ___yes___

16. Let's explore these operations a little further. What number is

    represented by $3 \circledast (4 \oplus 2)$? ___3375___

17. What number is represented by $(3 \circledast 4) \oplus (3 \circledast 2)$? ___585___

18. Is the operation $\circledast$ actually distributive over the operation $\oplus$? ___no___

Figurate Numbers

The numbers below are called **pentagonal numbers.** They are
the numbers of dots or disks that can be arranged as pentagons.

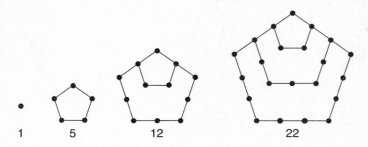

1   5   12   22

1. Evaluate the expression $\frac{1}{2}n(3n - 1)$ for values of n from
   1 through 4.

2. What do you notice?

3. Find the next six pentagonal numbers.

4. Evaluate the expression $\frac{1}{2}n(n + 1)$ for values of n from
   1 through 5. On another sheet of paper, make drawings to show
   why these numbers are called the triangular numbers.

5. Evaluate the expression $n(2n - 1)$ for values of n from
   1 through 5. Draw these hexagonal numbers.

6. Find the first 5 square numbers. Also, write the general
   expression for any square number.

The numbers you have explored above are called the plane
figure numbers because they can be arranged to make
geometric figures. You can also create solid figurate numbers.

7. If you pile 10 oranges into a pyramid with a triangle as a base,
   you get one of the tetrahedral numbers. How many layers are
   there in the pyramid? How many oranges are there in the
   bottom layers?

8. Evaluate the expression $\frac{1}{6}n(n + 1)(n + 2)$ for values of n from
   1 through 5 to find the first five tetrahedral numbers.

Enrichment

Figurate Numbers

The numbers below are called **pentagonal numbers.** They are
the numbers of dots or disks that can be arranged as pentagons.

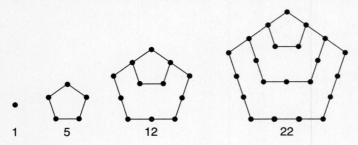

1   5   12   22

1. Evaluate the expression $\frac{1}{2}n(3n - 1)$ for values of n from
   1 through 4. **1, 5, 12, 22**

2. What do you notice? **They are the first four pentagonal numbers.**

3. Find the next six pentagonal numbers. **35, 51, 70, 92, 117, 145**

4. Evaluate the expression $\frac{1}{2}n(n + 1)$ for values of n from
   1 through 5. On another sheet of paper, make drawings to show
   why these numbers are called the triangular numbers. **1, 3, 6, 10, 15**

5. Evaluate the expression $n(2n - 1)$ for values of n from
   1 through 5. Draw these hexagonal numbers. **1, 6, 15, 28, 45**

6. Find the first 5 square numbers. Also, write the general
   expression for any square number. **1, 4, 9, 16, 25; n^2**

The numbers you have explored above are called the plane
figurate numbers because they can be arranged to make
geometric figures. You can also create solid figurate numbers.

7. If you pile 10 oranges into a pyramid with a triangle as a base,
   you get one of the tetrahedral numbers. How many layers are
   there in the pyramid? How many oranges are there in the
   bottom layers? **3 layers; 6**

8. Evaluate the expression $\frac{1}{6}n(n + 1)(n + 2)$ for values of n from
   1 through 5 to find the first five tetrahedral numbers. **1, 4, 10, 20, 35**

NAME _____ DATE _____

Enrichment

Intersection and Union

The **intersection** of two sets is the set of elements that are in both of the sets. The intersection of sets A and B is written A ∩ B. The **union** of two sets is the set of elements in either A, or in B, or in both. The union is written A ∪ B.

In the drawings below, suppose A is the set of points inside the circle and B is the set of points inside the square. Then, the shaded areas show the intersection and union.

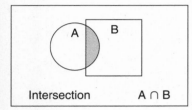

Intersection   A ∩ B

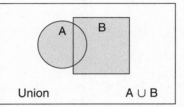

Union   A ∪ B

Write A ∩ B and A ∪ B for each of the following.

1. A = {p, q, r, s, t} B = {q, r, s} _____

2. A = {the integers between 2 and 7} B = {0, 3, 8} _____

3. A = {the states whose names start with K}
B = {the states whose capital is Honolulu or Topeka} _____

4. A = {the positive integer factors of 24}
B = {the counting numbers less than 10} _____

Suppose A = {numbers x such that x < 3}, B = {numbers x such as x ≥ −1}, and C = {numbers x such that x ≤ 1.5}. Graph each of the following.

5. A ∩ B

6. A ∪ B

7. A ∪ B

8. B ∩ C

9. (A ∩ C) ∩ B

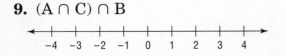

10. A ∩ (B ∪ C)

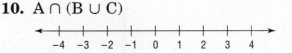

Algebra 1

2-1

Enrichment

Intersection and Union

The **intersection** of two sets is the set of elements that are in both of the sets. The intersection of sets A and B is written A ∩ B. The **union** of two sets is the set of elements in either A, or in B, or in both. The union is written A ∪ B.

In the drawings below, suppose A is the set of points inside the circle and B is the set of points inside the square. Then, the shaded areas show the intersection and union.

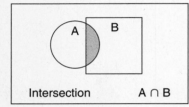
Intersection   A ∩ B

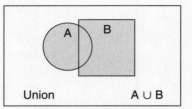
Union   A ∪ B

Write A ∩ B and A ∪ B *for each of the following.*

1. A = {p, q, r, s, t}   B = {q, r, s} _____ A ∩ B = {q, r, s} A ∪ B = {p, q, r, s, t}

2. A = {the integers between 2 and 7} B = {0, 3, 8} $\frac{A ∩ B = \{3\}}{A ∪ B = \{0, 3, 4, 5, 6, 8\}}$

3. A = {the states whose names start with K}   A ∩ B = {Kansas}
   B = {the states whose capital is Honolulu or Topeka} _____ A ∪ B = {Hawaii, Kansas, Kentucky}

4. A = {the positive integer factors of 24}   A ∩ B = {1, 2, 3, 4, 6, 8}
   B = {the counting numbers less than 10} ——— A ∪ B = {1, 2, 3, 4, 5, 6, 7, 8, 9, 12, 24}

Suppose A = *{numbers x such that x < 3},* B = *{numbers x such as x ≥ − 1},* and C = *{numbers x such that x ≤ 1.5}.* Graph each of the following.

5. A ∩ B

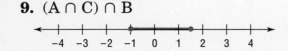

6. A ∪ B

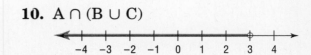

7. A ∪ B

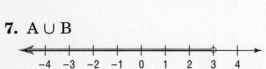

8. B ∩ C

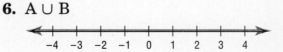

9. (A ∩ C) ∩ B

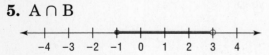

10. A ∩ (B ∪ C)

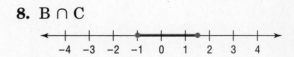

               Algebra 1

The Digits of π

The number π (pi) is the ratio of the
circumference of a circle to its diameter.
It is a nonrepeating and nonterminating
decimal. No block of the digits of π ever
repeats. Here are the first 201 digits of
π including 200 digits that follow the
decimal point.

3.14159	26535	89793	23846
69399	37510	58209	74944
86280	34825	34211	70679
09384	46095	50582	23172
84102	70193	85211	05559
26433	83279	50288	41971
59230	78164	06286	20899
82148	08651	32823	06647
53594	08128	34111	74502
64462	29489	54930	38196

Solve each problem.

1. If each of the digits appeared with equal frequency, how
   many times would each digit appear in the first 200 places
   following the decimal point?

2. Complete this frequency distribution table for the first 200
   digits of π that follow the decimal point.

Digit	Frequency (Tally Marks)	Frequency (Number)	Cumulative Frequency
0			
1			
2			
3			
4			
5			
6			
7			
8			
9			

3. Explain how the cumulative frequency column can be used
   to check a project like this one.

4. Which digit(s) appears most often?

5. Which digit(s) appears least often?

Algebra 1

Enrichment

The Digits of π

The number π (pi) is the ratio of the circumference of a circle to its diameter. It is a nonrepeating and nonterminating decimal. No block of the digits of π ever repeats. Here are the first 201 digits of π including 200 digits that follow the decimal point.

3.14159	26535	89793	23846
69399	37510	58209	74944
86280	34825	34211	70679
09384	46095	50582	23172
84102	70193	85211	05559
26433	83279	50288	41971
59230	78164	06286	20899
82148	08651	32823	06647
53594	08128	34111	74502
64462	29489	54930	38196

Solve each problem.

1. If each of the digits appeared with equal frequency, how many times would each digit appear in the first 200 places following the decimal point? **20**

2. Complete this frequency distribution table for the first 200 digits of π that follow the decimal point.

Digit	Frequency (Tally Marks)	Frequency (Number)	Cumulative Frequency
0	⅂HⅣ ⅂HⅣ ⅂HⅣ ////	19	19
1	⅂HⅣ ⅂HⅣ ⅂HⅣ ⅂HⅣ	20	39
2	⅂HⅣ ⅂HⅣ ⅂HⅣ ⅂HⅣ ////	24	63
3	⅂HⅣ ⅂HⅣ ⅂HⅣ ⅂HⅣ	20	83
4	⅂HⅣ ⅂HⅣ ⅂HⅣ ⅂HⅣ //	22	105
5	⅂HⅣ ⅂HⅣ ⅂HⅣ ⅂HⅣ	20	125
6	⅂HⅣ ⅂HⅣ ⅂HⅣ /	16	141
7	⅂HⅣ ⅂HⅣ //	12	153
8	⅂HⅣ ⅂HⅣ ⅂HⅣ ⅂HⅣ ////	24	177
9	⅂HⅣ ⅂HⅣ ⅂HⅣ ⅂HⅣ ///	23	200

3. Explain how the cumulative frequency column can be used to check a project like this one. **The last number should be 200, the number of items being counted.**

4. Which digit(s) appears most often? **2 and 8**

5. Which digit(s) appears least often? **7**

Algebra 1

Enrichment

Equivalent Sets

Two sets are **equal,** or identical, if they contain exactly the same elements. The order in which we name the elements is unimportant. Thus, {a, b, c, d} and {c, a, d, b} are equal sets. Two sets are **equivalent** if for every element of one set there is one and only one element in the other set; that is, there exists a one-to-one matching between the elements of the two sets. The one-to-one matchings below show that the sets are equivalent.

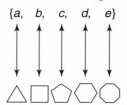

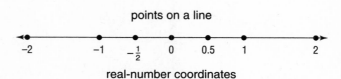

points on a line

real-number coordinates

Consider these equivalent sets.
Set of whole numbers =
{0, 1, 2, 3, 4, 5, ⋯}

Set of even whole numbers =
{0, 2, 4, 6, 8, 10, ⋯}

Are there more whole numbers or more even whole numbers? Or might there be the same number of each, even though we have no counting number to tell how many?

A one-to-one matching of the whole numbers and the even whole numbers appears at the right. Each whole number n is matched with the even number $2n$, and each even number $2n$ is matched with the whole number n. Therefore, the two sets are equivalent. This means that there are as many even whole numbers as there are whole numbers.

$$\{0, 1, 2, 3, 4, 5, \cdots, n, \cdots\}$$
$$\updownarrow \updownarrow \updownarrow \updownarrow \updownarrow \updownarrow \qquad \searrow$$
$$\{0, 2, 4, 6, 8, 10, \cdots, 2n, \cdots\}$$

Use a one-to-one matching to show that the two sets are equivalent.

1. {Amy, Betsy, Carol, Dorothy} and {Al, Bob, Carl, David} _____

2. {1, 2, 3, 4, 5, ⋯} and {3, 6, 9, 12, 15, ⋯} _____

3. {−1, −2, −3, −4, ⋯} and {1, 2, 3, 4, ⋯} _____

4. {1, 2, 3, 4, 5, ⋯} and {1, 3, 5, 7, 9, ⋯} _____

Enrichment

Equivalent Sets

Two sets are **equal,** or identical, if they contain exactly the
same elements. The order in which we name the elements is
unimportant. Thus, $\{a, b, c, d\}$ and $\{c, a, d, b\}$ are equal sets. Two
sets are **equivalent** if for every element of one set there is one
and only one element in the other set; that is, there exists a
one-to-one matching between the elements of the two sets. The
one-to-one matchings below show that the sets are equivalent.

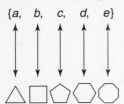

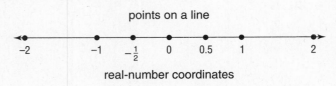

points on a line

real-number coordinates

Consider these equivalent sets.

Set of whole numbers =
$\{0, 1, 2, 3, 4, 5, \cdots\}$

Set of even whole numbers =
$\{0, 2, 4, 6, 8, 10, \cdots\}$

Are there more whole numbers or more even whole numbers? Or
might there be the same number of each, even though we have no
counting number to tell how many?

A one-to-one matching of the whole
numbers and the even whole numbers
appears at the right. Each whole number n
is matched with the even number $2n$, and
each even number $2n$ is matched with the
whole number n. Therefore, the two sets are equivalent. This
means that there are as many even whole numbers as there are
whole numbers.

$$\{0, 1, 2, 3, 4, 5, \cdots, n, \cdots\}$$
$$\updownarrow \updownarrow \updownarrow \updownarrow \updownarrow \updownarrow \qquad \searrow$$
$$\{0, 2, 4, 6, 8, 10, \cdots, 2n, \cdots\}$$

Use a one-to-one matching to show that the two sets are equivalent.

1. $\{$Amy, Betsy, Carol, Dorothy$\}$ and $\{$Al, Bob, Carl, David$\}$

$$\{\text{Amy, Betsy, Carol, Dorothy}\}$$
$$\updownarrow \qquad \updownarrow \qquad \updownarrow \qquad \updownarrow$$
$$\{\ \text{Al, \quad Bob, \quad Carl, \quad David}\ \}$$

2. $\{1, 2, 3, 4, 5, \cdots\}$ and $\{3, 6, 9, 12, 15, \cdots\}$

$$\{1, 2, 3, 4, 5, \cdots\}$$
$$\updownarrow \updownarrow \updownarrow \updownarrow \updownarrow$$
$$\{3, 6, 9, 12, 15, \cdots\}$$

3. $\{-1, -2, -3, -4, \cdots\}$ and $\{1, 2, 3, 4, \cdots\}$

$$\{-1, -2, -3, -4, \cdots\}$$
$$\updownarrow \updownarrow \updownarrow \updownarrow$$
$$\{\ 1, \ 2, \ 3, \ 4, \cdots\}$$

4. $\{1, 2, 3, 4, 5, \cdots\}$ and $\{1, 3, 5, 7, 9, \cdots\}$

$$\{1, 2, 3, 4, 5, \cdots\}$$
$$\updownarrow \updownarrow \updownarrow \updownarrow \updownarrow$$
$$\{1, 3, 5, 7, 9, \cdots\}$$

Algebra 1

Enrichment

Rounding Fractions

Rounding fractions is more difficult than rounding whole numbers or decimals. For example, think about how you would round $\frac{4}{9}$ inches to the nearest quarter-inch. Through estimation, you might realize that $\frac{4}{9}$ is less than $\frac{1}{2}$. But, is it closer to $\frac{1}{2}$ or to $\frac{1}{4}$? Here are two ways to round fractions. Example 1 uses only the fractions; Example 2 uses decimals.

Example 1:

Subtract the fraction twice. Use the two nearest quarters.

$$\frac{1}{2} - \frac{4}{9} = \frac{1}{18} \qquad \frac{4}{9} - \frac{1}{4} = \frac{7}{36}$$

Compare the differences.

$$\frac{1}{18} < \frac{7}{36}$$

The smaller difference shows you which fraction to round to.

$\frac{4}{9}$ rounds to $\frac{1}{2}$.

Example 2:

Change the fraction and the two nearest quarters to decimals.

$$\frac{4}{9} = 0.4\overline{4}, \frac{1}{2} = 0.5, \frac{1}{4} = 0.25$$

Find the decimal halfway between the two nearest quarters.

$$\frac{1}{2}(0.5 + 0.25) = 0.375$$

If the fraction is greater than the halfway decimal, round up. If not, round down.

$0.4\overline{4} > 0.3675$. So, $\frac{4}{9}$ is more than half way between $\frac{1}{4}$ and $\frac{1}{2}$.

$\frac{4}{9}$ rounds to $\frac{1}{2}$.

Round each fraction to the nearest one-quarter. Use either method.

1. $\frac{1}{3}$

2. $\frac{3}{7}$

3. $\frac{7}{11}$

4. $\frac{4}{15}$

5. $\frac{7}{20}$

6. $\frac{31}{50}$

7. $\frac{9}{25}$

8. $\frac{23}{30}$

Round each decimal or fraction to the nearest one-eighth.

9. 0.6

10. 0.1

11. 0.45

12. 0.85

13. $\frac{5}{7}$

14. $\frac{3}{20}$

15. $\frac{23}{25}$

16. $\frac{5}{9}$

Enrichment

Rounding Fractions

Rounding fractions is more difficult than rounding whole numbers or decimals. For example, think about how you would round $\frac{4}{9}$ inches to the nearest quarter-inch. Through estimation, you might realize that $\frac{4}{9}$ is less than $\frac{1}{2}$. But, is it closer to $\frac{1}{2}$ or to $\frac{1}{4}$? Here are two ways to round fractions. Example 1 uses only the fractions; Example 2 uses decimals.

Example 1:

Subtract the fraction twice. Use the two nearest quarters.

$$\frac{1}{2} - \frac{4}{9} = \frac{1}{18} \qquad \frac{4}{9} - \frac{1}{4} = \frac{7}{36}$$

Compare the differences.

$$\frac{1}{18} < \frac{7}{36}$$

The smaller difference shows you which fraction to round to.

$\frac{4}{9}$ rounds to $\frac{1}{2}$.

Example 2:

Change the fraction and the two nearest quarters to decimals.

$$\frac{4}{9} = 0.4\overline{4}, \frac{1}{2} = 0.5, \frac{1}{4} = 0.25$$

Find the decimal halfway between the two nearest quarters.

$$\frac{1}{2}(0.5 + 0.25) = 0.375$$

If the fraction is greater than the halfway decimal, round up. If not, round down.

$0.4\overline{4} > 0.3675$. So, $\frac{4}{9}$ is more than half way between $\frac{1}{4}$ and $\frac{1}{2}$.

$\frac{4}{9}$ rounds to $\frac{1}{2}$.

Round each fraction to the nearest one-quarter. Use either method.

1. $\frac{1}{3}$ $\frac{1}{4}$

2. $\frac{3}{7}$ $\frac{1}{2}$

3. $\frac{7}{11}$ $\frac{3}{4}$

4. $\frac{4}{15}$ $\frac{1}{4}$

5. $\frac{7}{20}$ $\frac{1}{4}$

6. $\frac{31}{50}$ $\frac{1}{2}$

7. $\frac{9}{25}$ $\frac{1}{4}$

8. $\frac{23}{30}$ $\frac{3}{4}$

Round each decimal or fraction to the nearest one-eighth.

9. 0.6 $\frac{5}{8}$

10. 0.1 $\frac{1}{8}$

11. 0.45 $\frac{1}{2}$

12. 0.85 $\frac{7}{8}$

13. $\frac{5}{7}$ $\frac{3}{4}$

14. $\frac{3}{20}$ $\frac{1}{8}$

15. $\frac{23}{25}$ $\frac{7}{8}$

16. $\frac{5}{9}$ $\frac{1}{2}$

Algebra 1

NAME_____ DATE_____

Enrichment

Tangram Puzzles

These seven geometric figures are called **tans.** They are used in a very old Chinese puzzle called **tangrams.**

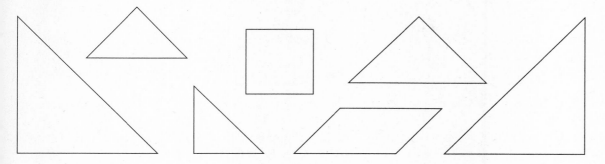

Glue the seven tans on heavy paper and cut them out. Use all seven pieces to make each shape shown. Record your solutions.

1. **2.** **3.**

4. **5.**

6. Each of the two figures is made from all seven tans. They seem to be exactly alike, but one has a foot and the other does not. Where does the second figure get his foot?

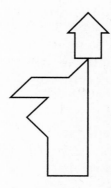 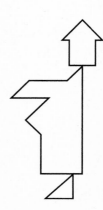

14

2-5

Enrichment

Tangram Puzzles

These seven geometric figures are called **tans.** They are used in
a very old Chinese puzzle called **tangrams.**

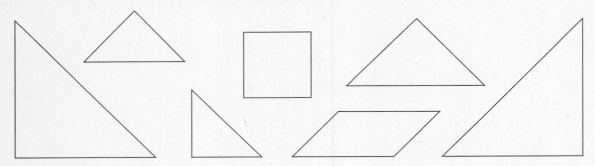

*Glue the seven tans on heavy paper and cut them out. Use all
seven pieces to make each shape shown. Record your solutions.*

1. 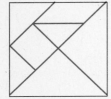   **2.** 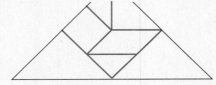   **3.**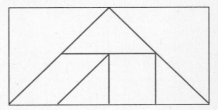

4. 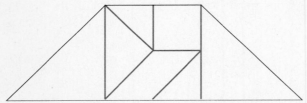   **5.**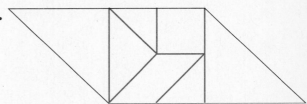

6. Each of the two figures is made from
all seven tans. They seem to be exactly
alike, but one has a foot and the other
does not. Where does the second figure
get his foot?
**In the left figure, the body is
made from 4 pieces rather
than 3. The extra piece
becomes the foot in the right
figure.**

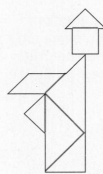
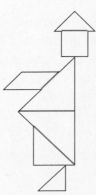

Algebra 1

Enrichment

Convergence, Divergence, and Limits

Imagine that a runner runs a mile from point A to point B. But, this is not an ordinary race! In the first minute, he runs one-half mile, reaching point C. In the next minute, he covers one-half the remaining distance, or $\frac{1}{4}$ mile, reaching point D. In the next minute he covers one-half the remaining distance, or $\frac{1}{8}$ mile, reaching point E.

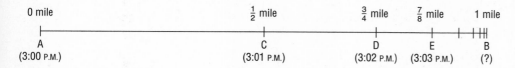

In this strange race, the runner approaches closer and closer to point B, but never gets there. However close he is to B, there is still some distance remaining, and in the next minute he can cover only half of that distance.

This race can be modeled by the infinite sequence

$$\frac{1}{2}, \frac{3}{4}, \frac{7}{8}, \frac{15}{16}, \cdots .$$

The terms of the sequence get closer and closer to 1. An infinite sequence that gets arbitrarily close to some number is said to **converge** to that number. The number is the limit of the sequence.

Not all infinite sequences converge. Those that do not are called **divergent**.

Write C if the sequence converges and D if it diverges. If the sequence converges, make a reasonable guess for its limit.

1. 2, 4, 6, 8, 10, ⋯ _____

2. 0, 3, 0, 3, 0, 3, ⋯ _____

3. $1, \frac{1}{2}, \frac{1}{3}, \frac{1}{4}, \frac{1}{5}, \cdots$ _____

4. 0.9, 0.99, 0.999, 0.9999, ⋯ _____

5. −5, 5, −5, 5, −5, 5, ⋯ _____

6. 0.1, 0.2, 0.3, 0.4, ⋯ _____

7. $2\frac{1}{4}, 2\frac{3}{4}, 2\frac{7}{8}, 2\frac{15}{16}, \cdots$ _____

8. $6, 5\frac{1}{2}, 5\frac{1}{3}, 5\frac{1}{4}, 5\frac{1}{5}, \cdots$ _____

9. 1, 4, 9, 16, 25, ⋯ _____

10. $1, -\frac{1}{2}, \frac{1}{3}, -\frac{1}{4}, \frac{1}{5}, -\frac{1}{6}, \cdots$ _____

11. Create one convergent sequence and one divergent sequence. Give the limit for your convergent sequence.

_____

Enrichment

Convergence, Divergence, and Limits

Imagine that a runner runs a mile from point A to point B. But, this is not an ordinary race! In the first minute, he runs one-half mile, reaching point C. In the next minute, he covers one-half the remaining distance, or $\frac{1}{4}$ mile, reaching point D. In the next minute he covers one-half the remaining distance, or $\frac{1}{8}$ mile, reaching point E.

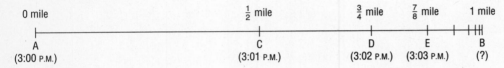

0 mile $\frac{1}{2}$ mile $\frac{3}{4}$ mile $\frac{7}{8}$ mile 1 mile

A   C   D   E   B
(3:00 P.M.)   (3:01 P.M.) (3:02 P.M.) (3:03 P.M.) (?)

In this strange race, the runner approaches closer and closer to point B, but never gets there. However close he is to B, there is still some distance remaining, and in the next minute he can cover only half of that distance.

This race can be modeled by the infinite sequence

$\frac{1}{2}, \frac{3}{4}, \frac{7}{8}, \frac{15}{16}, \cdots$

The terms of the sequence get closer and closer to 1. An infinite sequence that gets arbitrarily close to some number is said to **converge** to that number. The number is the limit of the sequence.

Not all infinite sequences converge. Those that do not are called **divergent**.

Write C if the sequence converges and D if it diverges. If the sequence converges, make a reasonable guess for its limit.

1. 2, 4, 6, 8, 10, $\cdots$ ___D___

2. 0, 3, 0, 3, 0, 3, $\cdots$ ___D___

3. 1, $\frac{1}{2}, \frac{1}{3}, \frac{1}{4}, \frac{1}{5}, \cdots$ ___C, 0___

4. 0.9, 0.99, 0.999, 0.9999, $\cdots$ ___C, 1___

5. $-5, 5, -5, 5, -5, 5, \cdots$ ___D___

6. 0.1, 0.2, 0.3, 0.4, $\cdots$ ___D___

7. $2\frac{1}{4}, 2\frac{3}{4}, 2\frac{7}{8}, 2\frac{15}{16}, \cdots$ ___C, 3___

8. 6, $5\frac{1}{2}, 5\frac{1}{3}, 5\frac{1}{4}, 5\frac{1}{5}, \cdots$ ___C, 5___

9. 1, 4, 9, 16, 25, $\cdots$ ___D___

10. 1, $-\frac{1}{2}, \frac{1}{3}, -\frac{1}{4}, \frac{1}{5}, -\frac{1}{6}, \cdots$ ___C, 0___

11. Create one convergent sequence and one divergent sequence. Give the limit for your convergent sequence.
Answers will vary.

NAME_____ DATE _____

Enrichment

Counterexamples

Some statements in mathematics can be proven false by
counterexamples. Consider the following statement.

For any numbers a and b, $a - b = b - a$.

You can prove that this statement is false in general if you can
find one example for which the statement is false.

Let $a = 7$ and $b = 3$. Substitute these values in the equation
above.

$$7 - 3 \stackrel{?}{=} 3 - 7$$
$$4 \neq -4$$

In general, for any numbers a and b, the statement $a - b = b - a$
is false. You can make the equivalent verbal statement:
subtraction is *not* a commutative operation.

**In each of the following exercises a, b, and c are any numbers.
Prove that the statement is false by counterexample.**

1. $a - (b - c) \stackrel{?}{=} (a - b) - c$

2. $a \div (b \div c) \stackrel{?}{=} (a \div b) \div c$

3. $a \div b \stackrel{?}{=} b \div a$

4. $a \div (b + c) \stackrel{?}{=} (a \div b) + (a \div c)$

5. $a + (bc) \stackrel{?}{=} (a + b)(a + c)$

6. $a^2 + a^2 \stackrel{?}{=} a^4$

7. Write the verbal equivalents for Exercises 1, 2, and 3.

8. For the distributive property $a(b + c) = ab + ac$ it is said
that multiplication distributes over addition. Exercises 4 and
5 prove that some operations do not distribute. Write a
statement for each exercise that indicates this.

Algebra 1

Enrichment

Counterexamples

Some statements in mathematics can be proven false by **counterexamples.** Consider the following statement.

For any numbers a and b, $a - b = b - a$.

You can prove that this statement is false in general if you can find one example for which the statement is false.

Let $a = 7$ and $b = 3$. Substitute these values in the equation above.

$$7 - 3 \stackrel{?}{=} 3 - 7$$
$$4 \neq -4$$

In general, for any numbers a and b, the statement $a - b = b - a$ is false. You can make the equivalent verbal statement: subtraction is *not* a commutative operation.

In each of the following exercises a, b, and c are any numbers. Prove that the statement is false by counterexample. Sample answers are given.

1. $a - (b - c) \stackrel{?}{=} (a - b) - c$
$6 - (4 - 2) \stackrel{?}{=} (6 - 4) - 2$
$6 - 2 \stackrel{?}{=} 2 - 2$
$4 \neq 0$

2. $a \div (b \div c) \stackrel{?}{=} (a \div b) \div c$
$6 \div (4 \div 2) \stackrel{?}{=} (6 \div 4) \div 2$
$\frac{6}{2} \stackrel{?}{=} \frac{1.5}{2}$
$3 \neq 0.75$

3. $a \div b \stackrel{?}{=} b \div a$
$6 \div 4 \stackrel{?}{=} 4 \div 6$
$\frac{3}{2} \neq \frac{2}{3}$

4. $a \div (b + c) \stackrel{?}{=} (a \div b) + (a \div c)$
$6 \div (4 + 2) \stackrel{?}{=} (6 \div 4) + (6 \div 2)$
$6 \div 6 \stackrel{?}{=} 1.5 + 3$
$1 \neq 4.5$

5. $a + (bc) \stackrel{?}{=} (a + b)(a + c)$
$6 + (4 \cdot 2) \stackrel{?}{=} (6 + 4)(6 + 2)$
$6 + 8 \stackrel{?}{=} (10)(8)$
$14 \neq 80$

6. $a^2 + a^2 \stackrel{?}{=} a^4$
$6^2 + 6^2 \stackrel{?}{=} 6^4$
$36 + 36 = 1296$
$72 \neq 1296$

7. Write the verbal equivalents for Exercises 1, 2, and 3.
1. Subtraction is not an associative operation.
2. Division is not an associative operation.
3. Division is not a commutative operation.

8. For the distributive property $a(b + c) = ab + ac$ it is said that multiplication distributes over addition. Exercises 4 and 5 prove that some operations do not distribute. Write a statement for each exercise that indicates this.
4. Division does not distribute over addition.
5. Addition does not distribute over multiplication.

Enrichment

Squares and Square Roots From a Graph

The graph of $y = x^2$ can be used to find the squares and square roots of numbers.

To find the square of 3, locate 3 on the x-axis. Then find its corresponding value on the y-axis.

The arrows show that $3^2 = 9$.

To find the square root of 4, first locate 4 on the y-axis. Then find its corresponding value on the x-axis. Following the arrows on the graph, you can see that $\sqrt{4} = 2$.

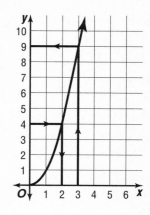

A small part of the graph at $y = x^2$ is shown below. A 1:10 ratio for unit length on the y-axis to unit length on the x-axis is used.

Example: Find $\sqrt{11}$.

The arrows show that $\sqrt{11} = 3.3$ to the nearest tenth.

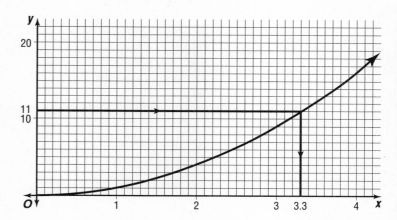

Use the graph above to find each of the following to the nearest whole number.

1. 1.5^2 **2.** 2.7^2 **3.** 0.9^2

4. 3.6^2 **5.** 4.2^2 **6.** 3.9^2

Use the graph above to find each of the following to the nearest tenth.

7. $\sqrt{15}$ **8.** $\sqrt{8}$ **9.** $\sqrt{3}$

10. $\sqrt{5}$ **11.** $\sqrt{14}$ **12.** $\sqrt{17}$

Enrichment

Squares and Square Roots From a Graph

The graph of $y = x^2$ can be used to find the squares and square roots of numbers.

To find the square of 3, locate 3 on the x-axis. Then find its corresponding value on the y-axis.

The arrows show that $3^2 = 9$.

To find the square root of 4, first locate 4 on the y-axis. Then find its corresponding value on the x-axis. Following the arrows on the graph, you can see that $\sqrt{4} = 2$.

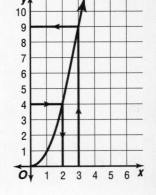

A small part of the graph at $y = x^2$ is shown below. A 1:10 ratio for unit length on the y-axis to unit length on the x-axis is used.

Example: Find $\sqrt{11}$.

The arrows show that $\sqrt{11} = 3.3$ to the nearest tenth.

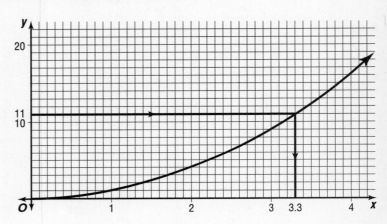

Use the graph above to find each of the following to the nearest whole number.

1. 1.5^2 **2**

2. 2.7^2 **7**

3. 0.9^2 **1**

4. 3.6^2 **13**

5. 4.2^2 **18**

6. 3.9^2 **15**

Use the graph above to find each of the following to the nearest tenth.

7. $\sqrt{15}$ **3.9**

8. $\sqrt{8}$ **2.8**

9. $\sqrt{3}$ **1.7**

10. $\sqrt{5}$ **2.2**

11. $\sqrt{14}$ **3.7**

12. $\sqrt{17}$ **4.1**

Enrichment

Formulas

Some consumers use the following formula when purchasing a new car.

$$d = 0.2(4s + c)$$ where d = the price the dealer paid the factory for the new car
s = the sticker price (the factory's suggested price)
and c = the cost for dealer preparation and shipping

1. What is the dealer cost for a car with a sticker price of $12,000 and costs for preparation and shipping of $320?

2. According to this formula, how much money does a dealer make if a car is sold for its sticker price of $9500 and the dealer pays $280 for shipping and preparation?

In *The 1978 Bill James Baseball Abstract,* the author introduced the "runs created" formula.

$$R = \frac{(h + w)t}{(b + w)}$$ where h = a player's number of hits
w = a player's number of walks
t = a player's number of total bases
b = a player's number of at-bats
and R = the approximate number of runs a team scores that are due to this player's actions

3. On June 15, 1983, the Seattle Mariners traded Julio Cruz to the Chicago White Sox for Tony Bernazard. Before the trade, these were the totals for each player.

	h	w	t	b	*runs created*
Cruz	46	20	64	181	_____
Bernazard	61	17	87	233	_____

Find the number of runs created by each player. Which player created more runs?

4. On August 10, 1983, the New York Yankees traded Jerry Mumphrey to the Houston Astros for Omar Moreno. Before the trade, these were the totals for each player.

	h	w	t	b	*runs created*
Mumphrey	70	28	132	267	_____
Moreno	98	8	132	405	_____

Find the number of runs created by each player.

2-9

Enrichment

Formulas

Some consumers use the following formula when purchasing a new car.

$$d = 0.2(4s + c)$$ where d = the price the dealer paid the factory for the new car
s = the sticker price (the factory's suggested price)
and c = the cost for dealer preparation and shipping

1. What is the dealer cost for a car with a sticker price of
$12,000 and costs for preparation and shipping of $320? **$9664**

2. According to this formula, how much money does a dealer
make if a car is sold for its sticker price of $9500 and the
dealer pays $280 for shipping and preparation? **$1844**

In *The 1978 Bill James Baseball Abstract,* the author introduced
the "runs created" formula.

$$R = \frac{(h + w)t}{(b + w)}$$ where h = a player's number of hits
w = a player's number of walks
t = a player's number of total bases
b = a player's number of at-bats
and R = the approximate number of runs a team scores that
are due to this player's actions

3. On June 15, 1983, the Seattle Mariners traded Julio Cruz to
the Chicago White Sox for Tony Bernazard. Before the trade,
these were the totals for each player.

	h	w	t	b	*runs created*
Cruz	46	20	64	181	21 runs
Bernazard	61	17	87	233	27 runs

Find the number of runs created by each player. Which
player created more runs? **Bernazard**

4. On August 10, 1983, the New York Yankees traded Jerry
Mumphrey to the Houston Astros for Omar Moreno. Before
the trade, these were the totals for each player.

	h	w	t	b	*runs created*
Mumphrey	70	28	132	267	44 runs
Moreno	98	8	132	405	34 runs

Find the number of runs created by each player.

Enrichment

Equations With No Solutions

Not every equation has a solution. Watch what happens when we try to solve the following equation.

$$8 - (3 - 2x) = 5x - 3x$$
$$8 - 3 + 2x = 2x$$
$$5 + 2x = 2x$$
$$5 = 0$$

Since the equation is equivalent to the false statement $5 = 0$, it has no solution. There is no value of x that will make the equation true.

Write a false statement that shows each equation has no solution.

1. $1 - 2t = 2(1 - t)$

2. $11y - 7y = 5 + 4y - 6$

3. $-7x^2 + 5 + 6x^2 = 12 - (2 + x^2)$

4. $2(2 - y^2) = 5 - (5 + 2y^2)$

5. $\frac{3}{2} + \frac{2}{3}p - 1 = \frac{1}{3}(1 + 2p)$

6. $0.5(1 + 3m) = 1.05 - (1 - 1.5m)$

Solve each equation if possible.

7. $5(3 - m) = 15m + 15$

8. $-9x + 12x = 3(2 - x)$

9. $10(0.2 + 0.4c) = 10c + 0.2 - 6c$

10. $13 - (3 - n) = 5(n + 2)$

11. $2(1 + 4t) = 8 - (3 - 8t)$

12. $3(d - 1) + 2 = 3(d + 2) - 5$

3-1

Enrichment

Equations With No Solutions

Not every equation has a solution. Watch what happens when
we try to solve the following equation.

$$8 - (3 - 2x) = 5x - 3x$$

$$8 - 3 + 2x = 2x$$

$$5 + 2x = 2x$$

$$5 = 0$$

Since the equation is equivalent to the false statement $5 = 0$, it
has no solution. There is no value of x that will make the
equation true.

**Write a false statement that shows each equation has no
solution.** **Answers may vary. Sample answers are given.**

1. $1 - 2t = 2(1 - t)$
1 = 2

2. $11y - 7y = 5 + 4y - 6$
0 = −1

3. $-7x^2 + 5 + 6x^2 = 12 - (2 + x^2)$
5 = 10

4. $2(2 - y^2) = 5 - (5 + 2y^2)$
4 = 0

5. $\frac{3}{2} + \frac{2}{3}p - 1 = \frac{1}{3}(1 + 2p)$
$\frac{1}{2} = \frac{1}{3}$

6. $0.5(1 + 3m) = 1.05 - (1 - 1.5m)$
0.5 = 0.05

Solve each equation if possible.

7. $5(3 - m) = 15m + 15$
m = 0

8. $-9x + 12x = 3(2 - x)$
x = 1

9. $10(0.2 + 0.4c) = 10c + 0.2 - 6c$
no solution

10. $13 - (3 - n) = 5(n + 2)$
n = 0

11. $2(1 + 4t) = 8 - (3 - 8t)$
no solution

12. $3(d - 1) + 2 = 3(d + 2) - 5$
no solution

Enrichment

Identities

Any equation that is true for every value of the variable is called an **identity.** When you try to solve an identity, you end up with a statement that is always true. Here is an example.

$$8 - (5 - 6x) = 3(1 + 2x)$$
$$8 - 5 + 6x = 3 + 6x$$
$$3 + 6x = 3 + 6x$$

State whether each equation is an identity. If it is not, find its solution.

1. $2(2 - 3x) = 3(3 + x) + 4$

2. $5(m + 1) + 6 = 3(4 + m) + (2m - 1)$

3. $(5t + 9) - (3t - 13) = 2(11 + t)$

4. $14 - (6 - 3c) = 4c - c$

5. $3y - 2(y + 19) = 9y - 3(9 - y)$

6. $3(3h - 1) = 4(h + 3)$

7. Start with the true statement $3x - 2 = 3x - 2$. Use it to create an identity of your own.

8. Start with the false statement $1 = 2$. Use it to create an equation with no solution.

NAME _____ DATE _____

Enrichment

Identities

Any equation that is true for every value of the variable is called an **identity.** When you try to solve an identity, you end up with a statement that is always true. Here is an example.

$$8 - (5 - 6x) = 3(1 + 2x)$$
$$8 - 5 + 6x = 3 + 6x$$
$$3 + 6x = 3 + 6x$$

State whether each equation is an identity. If it is not, find its solution.

1. $2(2 - 3x) = 3(3 + x) + 4$
   $x = -1$

2. $5(m + 1) + 6 = 3(4 + m) + (2m - 1)$
   identity

3. $(5t + 9) - (3t - 13) = 2(11 + t)$
   identity

4. $14 - (6 - 3c) = 4c - c$
   no solution

5. $3y - 2(y + 19) = 9y - 3(9 - y)$
   $y = -1$

6. $3(3h - 1) = 4(h + 3)$
   $h = 3$

7. Start with the true statement $3x - 2 = 3x - 2$. Use it to create an identity of your own. **Answers will vary.**

8. Start with the false statement $1 = 2$. Use it to create an equation with no solution. **Answers will vary.**

3-3

Enrichment

Division by Zero?

You may remember being told, "division by zero is not possible" or "division by zero is undefined" or "we never divide by zero." Have you wondered why this is so? Consider the two equations below.

$$\frac{5}{0} = n \qquad \frac{0}{0} = m$$

Because multiplication is the inverse of division, these lead to the following.

$$0 \cdot n = 5 \qquad 0 \cdot m = 0$$

There is no number that will make the first equation true. Any number at all will satisfy the second equation.

For each expression, give the values that must be excluded from the replacement set in order to prevent division by zero.

1. $\dfrac{x + 1}{x - 1}$
    2. $\dfrac{2(x + 1)}{2x - 1}$
    3. $\dfrac{(x + 1)(x - 1)}{(x + 2)(x - 2)}$

4. $\dfrac{x + y + 3}{(3x - 1)(3y - 1)}$
    5. $\dfrac{x^2 + y^2 + z^2}{2xyz}$
    6. $\dfrac{(x + y)^2}{x - y}$

Many demonstrations or "proofs" that lead to impossible results include a step involving division by zero. Explain what is wrong with each "proof" below.

7. $0 \cdot 1 = 0$ and $0 \cdot 2 = 0$.

Therefore, $\dfrac{0}{0} = 1$ and $\dfrac{0}{0} = 2$.

Therefore, $1 = 2$.

8. Assume that $a = b$.
Then $ab = a^2$
Therefore, $ab - b^2 = a^2 - b^2$.
Next it is shown that $a^2 - b^2 = (a + b)(a - b)$.
$(a + b)(a - b) = (a + b)\,a - (a + b)b$
$\qquad\qquad\quad = a^2 + ba - ab - b^2$
$\qquad\qquad\quad = a^2 + 0 - b^2$
$\qquad\qquad\quad = a^2 - b^2$
Therefore, $ab - b^2 = (a + b)(a - b)$.
Also, $b(a - b) = ba - b^2 = ab - b^2$.
Therefore, $b(a - b) = (a + b)(a - b)$.
Therefore, $b = a + b$.
Therefore, $b = 2b$.
Therefore, $1 = 2$.

Algebra 1

Division by Zero?

You may remember being told, "division by zero is not possible" or "division by zero is undefined" or "we never divide by zero." Have you wondered why this is so? Consider the two equations below.

$$\frac{5}{0} = n \qquad \frac{0}{0} = m$$

Because multiplication is the inverse of division, these lead to the following.

$$0 \cdot n = 5 \qquad 0 \cdot m = 0$$

There is no number that will make the first equation true. Any number at all will satisfy the second equation.

For each expression, give the values that must be excluded from the replacement set in order to prevent division by zero.

1. $\frac{x + 1}{x - 1}$ **$x = 1$**

2. $\frac{2(x + 1)}{2x - 1}$ **$x = \frac{1}{2}$**

3. $\frac{(x + 1)(x - 1)}{(x + 2)(x - 2)}$ **$x = -2$ or $x = 2$**

4. $\frac{x + y + 3}{(3x - 1)(3y - 1)}$ **$x = \frac{1}{3}, y = \frac{1}{3}$**

5. $\frac{x^2 + y^2 + z^2}{2xyz}$ **$x = 0, y = 0, z = 0$**

6. $\frac{(x + y)^2}{x - y}$ **values where $x = y$**

Many demonstrations or "proofs" that lead to impossible results include a step involving division by zero. Explain what is wrong with each "proof" below.

7. $0 \cdot 1 = 0$ and $0 \cdot 2 = 0$.
   Therefore, $\frac{0}{0} = 1$ and $\frac{0}{0} = 2$.
   Therefore, $1 = 2$.

   The second step involves division by zero.

8. Assume that $a = b$.
   Then $ab = a^2$
   Therefore, $ab - b^2 = a^2 - b^2$.
   Next it is shown that $a^2 - b^2 = (a + b)(a - b)$.
   $(a + b)(a - b) = (a + b)\, a - (a + b)b$
   $\qquad\qquad\quad = a^2 + ba - ab - b^2$
   $\qquad\qquad\quad = a^2 + 0 - b^2$
   $\qquad\qquad\quad = a^2 - b^2$
   Therefore, $ab - b^2 = (a + b)(a - b)$.
   Also, $b(a - b) = ba - b^2 = ab - b^2$.
   Therefore, $b(a - b) = (a + b)(a - b)$.
   Therefore, $b = a + b$.
   Therefore, $b = 2b$.
   Therefore, $1 = 2$.

   In moving to the third from the last step, each side is divided by $(a - b)$. Because $a = b$, that is dividing by zero.

3-4

Enrichment

Angles of a Triangle

In geometry, many statements about physical space are proven to be true. Such statements are called **theorems.** Here are two examples of geometric theorems.

a. The sum of the measures of the angles of a triangle is 180°.

b. If two sides of a triangle have equal measure, then the two angles opposite those sides also have equal measure.

For each of the triangles, solve for x. (A tick mark on two or more sides of a triangle indicates that the sides have equal measure.)

1.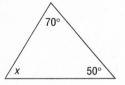

2.

3.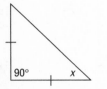

4.

5.

6.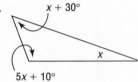

7.

8.

9.

10.

11. Two angles of a triangle have the same measure. The sum of the measures of these angles is one-half the measure of the third angle. Find the measures of the angles of the triangle.

12. The measure of one angle of a triangle is twice the measure of a second angle. The measure of the third angle is 12 less than the sum of the other two. Find the measures of the angles of the triangle.

Algebra 1

Enrichment

Angles of a Triangle

In geometry, many statements about physical space are proven to be true. Such statements are called **theorems.** Here are two examples of geometric theorems.

a. The sum of the measures of the angles of a triangle is 180°.

b. If two sides of a triangle have equal measure, then the two angles opposite those sides also have equal measure.

For each of the triangles, solve for x. (A tick mark on two or more sides of a triangle indicates that the sides have equal measure.)

1.
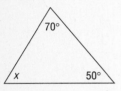

$x = 60°$

2.

$x = 45°$

3.
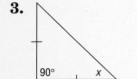

$x = 45°$

4.
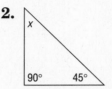

$x = 20°$

5.
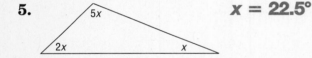

$x = 22.5°$

6.

$x = 10°$

7.
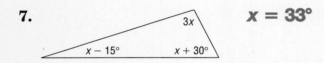

$x = 33°$

8.

$x = 100°$

9.

$x = 60°$

10.

$x = 50°$

11. Two angles of a triangle have the same measure. The sum of the measures of these angles is one-half the measure of the third angle. Find the measures of the angles of the triangle.
30°, 30°, 120°

12. The measure of one angle of a triangle is twice the measure of a second angle. The measure of the third angle is 12 less than the sum of the other two. Find the measures of the angles of the triangle.
64°, 32°, 84°

Enrichment

Using Equations

Use what you have learned about equations to solve each problem.

1. In many universities, grade point averages are figured out using a table like this.

grade	A	B	C	D	F
point value	4	3	2	1	0

Different classes often meet for a different number of hours each week. If you had the following schedule and grades, your average would be 2.45.

Course	Hours	Grade
Chemistry	3	C
Chemistry Lab	2	F
Calculus	5	A
Phys. Ed.	1	C
Total	11	

$$\frac{3(2) + 2(0) + 5(4) + 1(2)}{11} = \frac{28}{11} = 2.54$$

Suppose you are taking the following courses and you know all your grades but your math grade. What is the lowest math grade you could receive and still have a grade point average of over 3.00?

Course	Hours	Grade
Biology	5	A
Spanish	3	B
Math	4	?
English	4	B
Phys. Ed.	1	D
Total	17	

2. Read the information below the soccer standings at the right to understand how a team's points are determined. A shootout is a form of tie-breaker used when the score is still tied after an overtime period.

   a. A team had 5 wins, 2 shootout victories and 23 bonus points. Show that the number of points must be 61.

   b. To find the number of shootout victories for Golden Bay, let x = number of shootout victories. Then, $5 - x$ = number of regulation or overtime wins.
   $$6(5 - x) + 4x + 32 = 60$$
   Solve this equation.

   c. Find the number of shootout victories for Chicago.

Soccer

NASL

Eastern Division	W	L	GF	GA	BP	Pts.
Chicago	10	9	42	40	42	94
Cosmos	10	6	31	27	29	89
Toronto	8	8	33	22	29	71
Tampa Bay	7	12	31	49	27	67

Western Division	W	L	GF	GA	BP	Pts.
Vancouver	11	6	39	33	32	96
Minnesota	10	6	30	30	26	82
San Diego	9	9	33	38	27	75
Tulsa	7	10	31	32	29	71
Golden Bay	5	11	43	42	32	60

Six points are awarded for a regulation or overtime win, four points for a shootout victory, and one bonus point for every goal scored with a maximum of three per game. No bonus point is awarded for overtime or shootout goals.

Enrichment

Using Equations

Use what you have learned about equations to solve each problem.

1. In many universities, grade point averages are figured out using a table like this.

grade	A	B	C	D	F
point value	4	3	2	1	0

Different classes often meet for a different number of hours each week. If you had the following schedule and grades, your average would be 2.45.

Course	Hours	Grade
Chemistry	3	C
Chemistry Lab	2	F
Calculus	5	A
Phys. Ed.	1	C
Total	11	

$$\frac{3(2) + 2(0) + 5(4) + 1(2)}{11} = \frac{28}{11} = 2.54$$

Suppose you are taking the following courses and you know all your grades but your math grade. What is the lowest math grade you could receive and still have a grade point average of over 3.00? **B**

Course	Hours	Grade
Biology	5	A
Spanish	3	B
Math	4	?
English	4	B
Phys. Ed.	1	D
Total	17	

2. Read the information below the soccer standings at the right to understand how a team's points are determined. A shootout is a form of tie-breaker used when the score is still tied after an overtime period.

   a. A team had 5 wins, 2 shootout victories and 23 bonus points. Show that the number of points must be 61.
   6(5) + 4(2) + 23 = 61

   b. To find the number of shootout victories for Golden Bay, let x = number of shootout victories. Then, $5 - x$ = number of regulation or overtime wins. **30 − 6x + 4x + 32 = 60**
   $$6(5 - x) + 4x + 32 = 60$$
   −2x = −2
   x = 1
   Solve this equation.

   c. Find the number of shootout victories for Chicago.
   6(10 − x) + 4x + 42 = 94
   60 − 6x + 4x + 42 = 94
   −2x = −8
   x = 4

Soccer

NASL

Eastern Division	W	L	GF	GA	BP	Pts.
Chicago	10	9	42	40	42	94
Cosmos	10	6	31	27	29	89
Toronto	8	8	33	22	29	71
Tampa Bay	7	12	31	49	27	67

Western Division	W	L	GF	GA	BP	Pts.
Vancouver	11	6	39	33	32	96
Minnesota	10	6	30	30	26	82
San Diego	9	9	33	38	27	75
Tulsa	7	10	31	32	29	71
Golden Bay	5	11	43	42	32	60

Six points are awarded for a regulation or overtime win, four points for a shootout victory, and one bonus point for every goal scored with a maximum of three per game. No bonus point is awarded for overtime or shootout goals.

Enrichment

Diophantine Equations

The first great algebraist, Diophantus of Alexandria (about A.D. 300), devoted much of his work to the solving of indeterminate equations. An indeterminate equation has more than one variable and an unlimited number of solutions. An example is $x + 2y = 4$.

When the coefficients of an indeterminate equation are integers and you are asked to find solutions that must be integers, the equation is called *diophantine*. Such equations can be quite difficult to solve, often involving trial and error—and some luck!

Solve each diophantine equation by finding at least one pair of positive integers that makes the equation true. Some hints are given to help you.

1. $2x + 5y = 32$

   a. First solve the equation for x.

   b. Why must y be an even number?

   c. Find at least one solution.

2. $5x + 2y = 42$

   a. First solve the equation for x.

   b. Rewrite your answer in the form $x = 8 +$ some expression.

   c. Why must $(2 - 2y)$ be a multiple of 5?

   d. Find at least one solution.

3. $2x + 7y = 29$

4. $7x + 5y = 118$

5. $8x - 13y = 100$

6. $3x + 4y = 22$

7. $5x - 14y = 11$

8. $7x + 3y = 40$

Algebra 1

Diophantine Equations

The first great algebraist, Diophantus of Alexandria (about A.D. 300), devoted much of his work to the solving of indeterminate equations. An indeterminate equation has more than one variable and an unlimited number of solutions. An example is $x + 2y = 4$.

When the coefficients of an indeterminate equation are integers and you are asked to find solutions that must be integers, the equation is called *diophantine*. Such equations can be quite difficult to solve, often involving trial and error—and some luck!

Solve each diophantine equation by finding at least one pair of positive integers that makes the equation true. Some hints are given to help you.

1. $2x + 5y = 32$

   a. First solve the equation for x. $x = 16 - \dfrac{5y}{2}$

   b. Why must y be an even number? **If y is odd, then x won't be an integer.**

   c. Find at least one solution. **Any of these: (11, 2), (6, 4), (1, 6)**

2. $5x + 2y = 42$

   a. First solve the equation for x. $x = \dfrac{42 - 2y}{5}$

   b. Rewrite your answer in the form $x = 8 +$ some expression. $x = 8 + \dfrac{2 - 2y}{5}$

   c. Why must $(2 - 2y)$ be a multiple of 5? **Otherwise, x won't be an integer.**

   d. Find at least one solution. **Any of these: (8, 1), (6, 6), (4, 11), (2, 16)**

3. $2x + 7y = 29$
(11, 1) or (4, 3)

4. $7x + 5y = 118$
Any of these: (14, 4), (9, 11), (4, 18)

5. $8x - 13y = 100$
(19, 4), (32, 12) or any pair when $y = 4n$ and n is a positive odd number

6. $3x + 4y = 22$
(6, 1) or (2, 4)

7. $5x - 14y = 11$
(5, 1), (19, 6) or any pair when $y = 5m - 4$ and m is a positive number

8. $7x + 3y = 40$
(4, 4) or (1, 11)

Other Kinds of Means

There are many different kinds of means besides the arithmetic mean. A mean for a set of numbers has these two properties:

a. It typifies or represents the set.

b. It is not less than the least number and it is not greater than the greatest number.

Here are the formulas for the arithmetic mean and three other means.

Arithmetic Mean
Add the numbers in the set. Then divide the sum by n, the number of elements in the set.

$$\frac{x_1 + x_2 + x_3 + \cdots + x_n}{n}$$

Geometric Mean
Multiply all the numbers in the set. Then find the nth root of their product.

$$\sqrt[n]{x_1 \cdot x_2 \cdot x_3 \cdot \cdots \cdot x_n}$$

Harmonic Mean
Divide the number of elements in the set by the sum of the reciprocals of the numbers.

$$\frac{n}{\dfrac{1}{x_1} + \dfrac{1}{x_2} + \dfrac{1}{x_3} + \cdots + \dfrac{1}{x_n}}$$

Quadratic Mean
Add the squares of the numbers. Divide their sum by the number in the set. Then, take the square root.

$$\sqrt{\frac{x_1^2 + x_2^2 + x_3^2 + \cdots + x_n^2}{n}}$$

Find the four different means for each set of numbers.

1. 10, 100

2. 50, 60

3. 1, 2, 3, 4, 5,

4. 2, 2, 4, 4

5. Use the results from Exercises 1 to 4 to compare the relative sizes of the four types of means.

3-7

Enrichment

Other Kinds of Means

There are many different kinds of means besides the arithmetic mean. A mean for a set of numbers has these two properties:

a. It typifies or represents the set.

b. It is not less than the least number and it is not greater than the greatest number.

Here are the formulas for the arithmetic mean and three other means.

Arithmetic Mean
Add the numbers in the set. Then divide the sum by n, the number of elements in the set.

$$\frac{x_1 + x_2 + x_3 + \cdots + x_n}{n}$$

Geometric Mean
Multiply all the numbers in the set. Then find the nth root of their product.

$$\sqrt[n]{x_1 \cdot x_2 \cdot x_3 \cdot \cdots \cdot x_n}$$

Harmonic Mean
Divide the number of elements in the set by the sum of the reciprocals of the numbers.

$$\frac{n}{\dfrac{1}{x_1} + \dfrac{1}{x_2} + \dfrac{1}{x_3} + \cdots + \dfrac{1}{x_n}}$$

Quadratic Mean
Add the squares of the numbers. Divide their sum by the number in the set. Then, take the square root.

$$\sqrt{\frac{x_1^2 + x_2^2 + x_3^2 + \cdots + x_n^2}{n}}$$

Find the four different means for each set of numbers.

1. 10, 100
$A = 55$ $G = 31.62$
$H = 18.18$ $Q = 71.06$

2. 50, 60
$A = 55$ $G = 54.77$
$H = 54.55$ $Q = 55.23$

3. 1, 2, 3, 4, 5,
$A = 3$ $G = 2.61$
$H = 2.19$ $Q = 3.32$

4. 2, 2, 4, 4
$A = 3$ $G = 2.83$
$H = 2.67$ $Q = 3.16$

5. Use the results from Exercises 1 to 4 to compare the relative sizes of the four types of means.
From least to greatest, the means are the harmonic, geometric, arithmetic, and quadratic means.

Scale Drawings

The map at the left below shows building lots for sale. The scale ratio is 1:2400. At the right below is the floor plan for a two-bedroom apartment. The length of the living room is 6 m. On the plan the living room is 6 cm long.

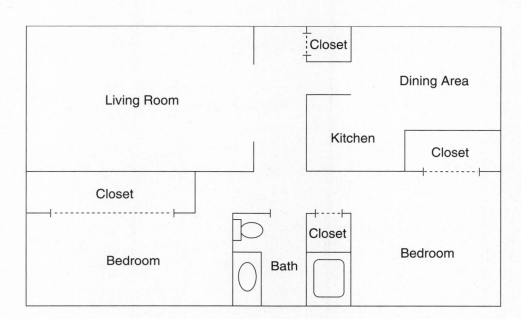

Answer each question.

1. On the map, how many feet are represented by an inch?

2. On the map, measure the frontage of Lot 2 on Sylvan Road in inches. What is the actual frontage in feet?

3. What is the scale ratio represented on the floor plan?

4. On the floor plan, measure the width of the living room in centimeters. What is the actual width in meters?

5. About how many square meters of carpeting would be needed to carpet the living room?

6. Make a scale drawing of your classroom using an appropriate scale.

7. On the scale for a map of Lancaster, Pennsylvania, 2.5 cm equals 3 km. Find the scale ratio.

NAME _____ DATE _____

Enrichment

Scale Drawings

The map at the left below shows building lots for sale. The scale ratio is 1:2400. At the right below is the floor plan for a two-bedroom apartment. The length of the living room is 6 m. On the plan the living room is 6 cm long.

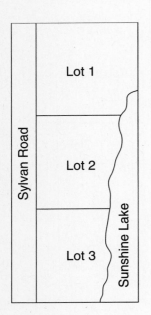
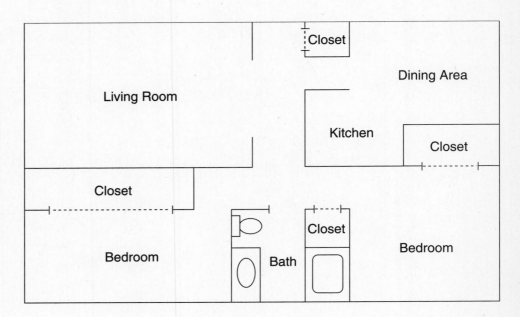

Answer each question.

1. On the map, how many feet are represented by an inch? **200 ft**

2. On the map, measure the frontage of Lot 2 on Sylvan Road in inches. What is the actual frontage in feet? **200 ft**

3. What is the scale ratio represented on the floor plan? **1:100**

4. On the floor plan, measure the width of the living room in centimeters. What is the actual width in meters? **4 m**

5. About how many square meters of carpeting would be needed to carpet the living room? **24 m²**

6. Make a scale drawing of your classroom using an appropriate scale. **Answers will vary.**

7. On the scale for a map of Lancaster, Pennsylvania, 2.5 cm equals 3 km. Find the scale ratio. **1:120,000**

Algebra 1

Enrichment

A Curious Construction

Many mathematicians have been
interested in ways to construct the
number π. Here is one such geometric
construction.

In the drawing, triangles ABC and ADE
are right triangles. The length of $\overline{AD}$
equals the length of $\overline{AC}$ and $\overline{FB}$ is
parallel to $\overline{EG}$.

The length of $\overline{BG}$ gives a decimal
approximation of the fractional part of π
to six decimal places.

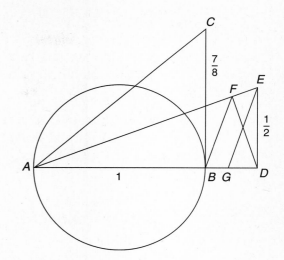

Follow the steps to find the length of $\overline{BG}$.

1. Use the length of $\overline{BC}$ and the Pythagorean theorem to find
   the length of $\overline{AC}$.

2. Find the length of $\overline{AD}$.

3. Use the length of $\overline{AD}$ and the Pythagorean theorem to find
   the length of $\overline{AE}$.

4. The sides of the similar triangles FED and DEA are in
   proportion. So, $\dfrac{FE}{0.5} = \dfrac{0.5}{AE}$. Find the length of $\overline{FE}$.

5. Find the length of $\overline{AF}$.

6. The sides of the similar triangles AFB and AEG are in
   proportion. So, $\dfrac{AF}{AE} = \dfrac{AB}{AG}$. Find the length of $\overline{AG}$.

7. Now, find the length of $\overline{BG}$.

8. The value of π to seven decimal places is 3.1415927.
   Compare the fractional part of π with the length of $\overline{AG}$.

4-2

Enrichment

A Curious Construction

Many mathematicians have been interested in ways to construct the number π. Here is one such geometric construction.

In the drawing, triangles ABC and ADE are right triangles. The length of $\overline{AD}$ equals the length of $\overline{AC}$ and $\overline{FB}$ is parallel to $\overline{EG}$.

The length of $\overline{BG}$ gives a decimal approximation of the fractional part of π to six decimal places.

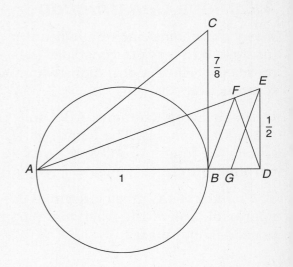

Follow the steps to find the length of $\overline{BG}$.

1. Use the length of $\overline{BC}$ and the Pythagorean theorem to find the length of $\overline{AC}$.
$$AC = \sqrt{1^2 + \left(\frac{7}{8}\right)^2} = 1.3287682$$

2. Find the length of $\overline{AD}$.
$$AD = AC = 1.3287682$$

3. Use the length of $\overline{AD}$ and the Pythagorean theorem to find the length of $\overline{AE}$.
$$AE = \sqrt{(AD)^2 + \left(\frac{1}{2}\right)^2} = 1.4197271$$

4. The sides of the similar triangles FED and DEA are in proportion. So, $\frac{FE}{0.5} = \frac{0.5}{AE}$. Find the length of $\overline{FE}$.
$$FE = \frac{1}{4(AE)} \quad FE = 0.1760902$$

5. Find the length of $\overline{AF}$.
$$AF = AE - FE = 1.2436369$$

6. The sides of the similar triangles AFB and AEG are in proportion. So, $\frac{AF}{AE} = \frac{AB}{AG}$. Find the length of $\overline{AG}$.
$$AG = \frac{AB \cdot AE}{AF} = \frac{AE}{AF} = 1.1415929$$

7. Now, find the length of $\overline{BG}$.
$$BG = AG - AB = AG - 1 = 0.1415929$$

8. The value of π to seven decimal places is 3.1415927. Compare the fractional part of π with the length of $\overline{AG}$.
0.1415929 − 0.1415927 = 0.0000002, an error of less than 1 part in a million

Modern Art

The painting below, aptly titled, "Right Triangles," was painted
by that well-known artist Two-loose La-Rectangle. Using the
information below, find the dimensions of this masterpiece.
(*Hint*: The triangle that includes $\angle F$ is isosceles.)

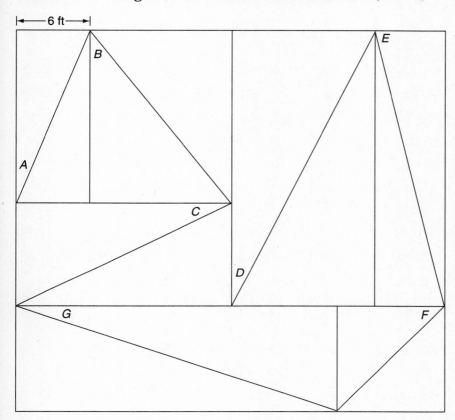

$$\tan A = \frac{2}{5} \qquad\qquad \tan B = \frac{4}{5} \qquad\qquad \tan C = \frac{1}{2}$$

$$\tan D = \frac{1}{2} \qquad\qquad \tan E = 4 \qquad\qquad \tan F = 1$$

$$\tan G = \frac{1}{3}$$

1. What is the length of the painting?

2. What is the width of the painting?

4-3

Enrichment

Modern Art

The painting below, aptly titled, "Right Triangles," was painted
by that well-known artist Two-loose La-Rectangle. Using the
information below, find the dimensions of this masterpiece.
(*Hint*: The triangle that includes $\angle F$ is isosceles.)

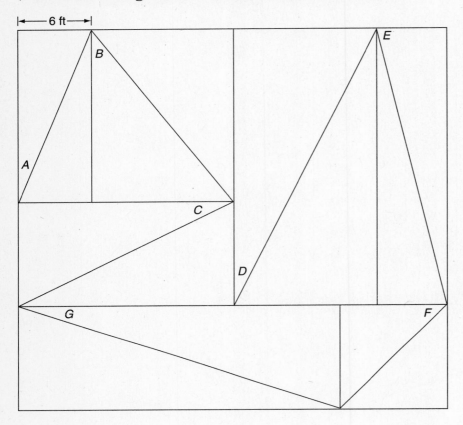

$\tan A = \dfrac{2}{5}$ $\qquad\qquad$ $\tan B = \dfrac{4}{5}$ $\qquad\qquad$ $\tan C = \dfrac{1}{2}$

$\tan D = \dfrac{1}{2}$ $\qquad\qquad$ $\tan E = 4$ $\qquad\qquad$ $\tan F = 1$

$\tan G = \dfrac{1}{3}$

1. What is the length of the painting? **33 ft**

2. What is the width of the painting? **36 ft**

Algebra 1

4-4

Enrichment

Compound Interest

In most banks, interest on savings accounts is compounded at set time periods such as three or six months. At the end of each period, the bank adds the interest earned to the account. During the next period, the bank pays interest on all the money in the bank, including interest. In this way, the account earns interest on interest.

Suppose Ms. Tanner has $1000 in an account that is compounded quarterly at 5%. Find the balance after the first two quarters.

Use $I = prt$ to find the interest earned in the first quarter if $p = 1000$ and $r = 5\%$. Why is t equal to $\frac{1}{4}$?

First quarter: $I = 1000 \times 0.05 \times \frac{1}{4}$

$I = 12.50$

The interest, $12.50, earned in the first quarter is added to $1000. The principal becomes $1012.50.

Second quarter: $I = 1012.50 \times 0.05 \times \frac{1}{4}$

$I = 12.65625$ The interest in the second quarter is $12.66.

The balance after two quarters is $1012.50 + 12.66 or $1025.16.

Answer each of the following questions.

1. How much interest is earned in the third quarter of Ms. Tanner's account?

2. What is the balance in her account after three quarters?

3. What is the balance in her account after one year?

4. Suppose Ms. Tanner's account is compounded semiannually. What is the balance at the end of six months?

5. What is the balance after one year if her account is compounded semiannually?

Compound Interest

In most banks, interest on savings accounts is compounded at set time periods such as three or six months. At the end of each period, the bank adds the interest earned to the account. During the next period, the bank pays interest on all the money in the bank, including interest. In this way, the account earns interest on interest.

Suppose Ms. Tanner has $1000 in an account that is compounded quarterly at 5%. Find the balance after the first two quarters.

Use $I = prt$ to find the interest earned in the first quarter if $p = 1000$ and $r = 5\%$. Why is t equal to $\frac{1}{4}$?

First quarter: $I = 1000 \times 0.05 \times \frac{1}{4}$

$\qquad I = 12.50$

The interest, $12.50, earned in the first quarter is added to $1000. The principal becomes $1012.50.

Second quarter: $I = 1012.50 \times 0.05 \times \frac{1}{4}$

$\qquad I = 12.65625$ The interest in the second quarter is $12.66.

The balance after two quarters is $1012.50 + 12.66 or $1025.16.

Answer each of the following questions.

1. How much interest is earned in the third quarter of Ms. Tanner's account? **$I = 12.81**

2. What is the balance in her account after three quarters?
   $1037.97

3. What is the balance in her account after one year?
   $1050.94

4. Suppose Ms. Tanner's account is compounded semiannually. What is the balance at the end of six months? **$1025.00**

5. What is the balance after one year if her account is compounded semiannually? **$1050.63**

Enrichment

Using Percent

Use what you have learned about percent to solve each problem.

A TV movie had a "rating" of 15 and a 25 "share." The rating of 15 means that 15% of the nation's total TV households were tuned in to this show. The 25 share means that 25% of the homes with TVs turned on were tuned to the movie. How many TV households had their TVs turned off at this time?

To find out, let T = the number of TV households
and x = the number of TV households with the TV off.
Then $T - x$ = the number of TV households with the TV on.

Since $0.15T$ and $0.25(T - x)$ both represent the number of households tuned to the movie,

$$0.15T = 0.25(T - x)$$
$$0.15T = 0.25T - 0.25x.$$

Solve for x.
$$0.25x = 0.10T$$
$$x = \frac{0.10T}{0.25} = 0.40T$$

Forty percent of the TV households had their TVs off when the movie was aired.

Answer each question.

1. During that same week, a sports broadcast had a rating of 22.1 and a 43 share. Show that the percent of TV households with their TVs off was about 48.6%.

2. Find the percent of TV households with their TVs turned off during a show with a rating of 18.9 and a 29 share.

3. Show that if T is the number of TV households, r is the rating, and s is the share, then the number of TV households with the TV off is $\frac{(s - r)T}{s}$.

4. If the fraction of TV households with no TV on is $\frac{s - r}{s}$ then show that the fraction of TV households with TVs on is $\frac{r}{s}$.

5. Find the percent of TV households with TVs on during the most watched serial program in history: the last episode of *M*A*S*H,* which had a 60.3 rating and a 77 share.

6. A local station now has a 2 share. Each share is worth $50,000 in advertising revenue per month. The station is thinking of going commercial free for the three months of summer to gain more listeners. What would its new share have to be for the last 4 months of the year to make more money for the year than it would have made had it not gone commercial free?

Enrichment

Using Percent

Use what you have learned about percent to solve each problem.

A TV movie had a "rating" of 15 and a 25 "share." The rating of 15 means that 15% of the nation's total TV households were tuned in to this show. The 25 share means that 25% of the homes with TVs turned on were tuned to the movie. How many TV households had their TVs turned off at this time?

To find out, let T = the number of TV households
and x = the number of TV households with the TV off.
Then $T - x$ = the number of TV households with the TV on.

Since $0.15T$ and $0.25(T - x)$ both represent the number of households tuned to the movie,

$$0.15T = 0.25(T - x)$$
$$0.15T = 0.25T - 0.25x.$$

Solve for x.
$$0.25x = 0.10T$$
$$x = \frac{0.10T}{0.25} = 0.40T$$

Forty percent of the TV households had their TVs off when the movie was aired.

Answer each question.

1. During that same week, a sports broadcast had a rating of 22.1 and a 43 share. Show that the percent of TV households with their TVs off was about 48.6%.

$$0.221T = 0.43T - 0.43x$$
$$x = \frac{0.221T - 0.43T}{-0.43}$$
$$= 0.486T$$

2. Find the percent of TV households with their TVs turned off during a show with a rating of 18.9 and a 29 share. **34.8%**

3. Show that if T is the number of TV households, r is the rating, and s is the share, then the number of TV households with the TV off is $\frac{(s - r)T}{s}$. **Solve $rT = s(T - x)$ for x.**

4. If the fraction of TV households with no TV on is $\frac{s - r}{s}$ then show that the fraction of TV households with TVs on is $\frac{r}{s}$. $1 - \frac{s-r}{s} = \frac{r}{s}$

5. Find the percent of TV households with TVs on during the most watched serial program in history: the last episode of $M*A*S*H$, which had a 60.3 rating and a 77 share. $\frac{60.3}{77} = 78.3\%$

6. A local station now has a 2 share. Each share is worth $50,000 in advertising revenue per month. The station is thinking of going commercial free for the three months of summer to gain more listeners. What would its new share have to be for the last 4 months of the year to make more money for the year than it would have made had it not gone commercial free? **greater than 3.5**

Enrichment

Geometric Probability

If a dart, thrown at random, hits a triangular board shown at the right, what is the probability that it will hit the shaded region? This probability can be determined by comparing the area of the shaded region to the area of the board. This ratio indicates what fraction of the tosses should hit in the shaded region.

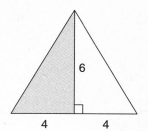

$$\frac{\text{area of shaded region}}{\text{area of triangular board}} = \frac{\frac{1}{2}(4)(6)}{\frac{1}{2}(8)(6)}$$

$$= \frac{12}{24} \text{ or } \frac{1}{2}$$

In general, if S is a subregion of some region R, then the probability, $P(S)$, that a point, chosen at random, belongs to subregion S is given by the following.

$$P(S) = \frac{\text{area of subregion } S}{\text{area of region } R}$$

Find the probability that a point, chosen at random, belongs to the shaded subregions of the following regions.

1.
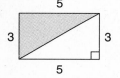

2.
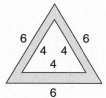

3.

4.
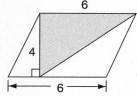

5.
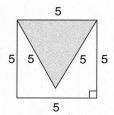

6.
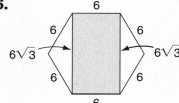

7.

8.
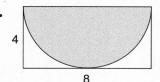

9.
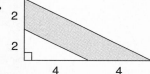

Enrichment

Geometric Probability

If a dart, thrown at random, hits a triangular board shown at the right, what is the probability that it will hit the shaded region? This probability can be determined by comparing the area of the shaded region to the area of the board. This ratio indicates what fraction of the tosses should hit in the shaded region.

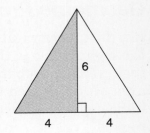

$$\frac{\text{area of shaded region}}{\text{area of triangular board}} = \frac{\frac{1}{2}(4)(6)}{\frac{1}{2}(8)(6)}$$

$$= \frac{12}{24} \text{ or } \frac{1}{2}$$

In general, if S is a subregion of some region R, then the probability, $P(S)$, that a point, chosen at random, belongs to subregion S is given by the following.

$$P(S) = \frac{\text{area of subregion } S}{\text{area of region } R}$$

Find the probability that a point, chosen at random, belongs to the shaded subregions of the following regions.

1.
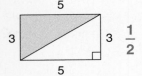
$\frac{1}{2}$

2.
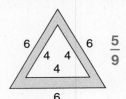
$\frac{5}{9}$

3.
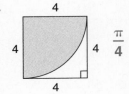
$\frac{\pi}{4}$

4.
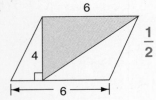
$\frac{1}{2}$

5.
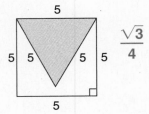
$\frac{\sqrt{3}}{4}$

6.
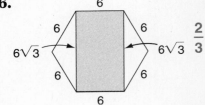
$\frac{2}{3}$

7.
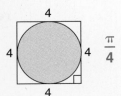
$\frac{\pi}{4}$

8.
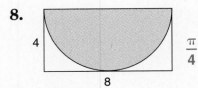
$\frac{\pi}{4}$

9.
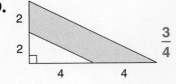
$\frac{3}{4}$

Algebra 1

Partnerships

Two or more people who agree to combine their money, goods,
or skill in some business often do so by forming a *partnership*.
Gains and losses in a partnership are usually divided in
proportion to the amount of money each person has invested.

Sharon and Tina start a business to print restaurant menus
using Tina's computer. For supplies and software, Sharon
invests $1200 and Tina, $800. If their profit after the first year
is $500, what is each person's share?

The entire investment is $1200 plus $800, or $2000.

Sharon's share is $\frac{\$1200}{\$2000}$, or $\frac{3}{5}$. Tina's share is $\frac{\$800}{\$2000}$, or $\frac{2}{5}$.

Answer each question.

1. In the problem above, what is Sharon's share of the profit?

2. What is Tina's share?

3. Sal and Mario were partners in a construction business. Sal put in $5000 and Mario, $4000. Their profit in 3 years was $4500. What was each partner's share?

4. Tim, Bob, and Alice entered into a business partnership for 2 years. Tim put in $3600, Bob put in $2400, and Alice put in $2000. If their profit was $3000, what was each person's share?

5. Fred, Vito, and Hal began with a capital of $28,000. Fred furnished $7000; Vito, $6000; and Hal, the remainder. If they gained 14% on their investment, what was each person's share?

6. A storeroom belonging to Taylor, Bartinelli, & Wong was entirely destroyed by fire. They received $9675 insurance. What was each person's share, if Taylor owned 15%, Bartinelli, 40%, and Wong the remainder?

7. Divide a profit of $7200 between two partners so that the ratio of the shares is 4 to 5.

8. Divide a profit of $18,000 among three partners so that the ratio of the shares is 1:2:3.

Enrichment

Partnerships

Two or more people who agree to combine their money, goods, or skill in some business often do so by forming a *partnership*. Gains and losses in a partnership are usually divided in proportion to the amount of money each person has invested.

Sharon and Tina start a business to print restaurant menus using Tina's computer. For supplies and software, Sharon invests $1200 and Tina, $800. If their profit after the first year is $500, what is each person's share?

The entire investment is $1200 plus $800, or $2000.

Sharon's share is $\frac{\$1200}{\$2238}$, or $\frac{3}{5}$. Tina's share is $\frac{\$800}{\$2238}$, or $\frac{2}{5}$.

Answer each question.

1. In the problem above, what is Sharon's share of the profit? **$300**

2. What is Tina's share? **$200**

3. Sal and Mario were partners in a construction business. Sal put in $5238 and Mario, $4238. Their profit in 3 years was $4500. What was each partner's share?
Sal: $2500; Mario: $2238

4. Tim, Bob, and Alice entered into a business partnership for 2 years. Tim put in $3600, Bob put in $2400, and Alice put in $2238. If their profit was $3238, what was each person's share?
Tim: $1350; Bob: $900; Alice: $750

5. Fred, Vito, and Hal began with a capital of $28,238. Fred furnished $7238; Vito, $6238; and Hal, the remainder. If they gained 14% on their investment, what was each person's share? **Fred: $980; Vito: $840; Hal: $2100**

6. A storeroom belonging to Taylor, Bartinelli, & Wong was entirely destroyed by fire. They received $9675 insurance. What was each person's share, if Taylor owned 15%, Bartinelli, 40%, and Wong the remainder?
Taylor: $1451.25; Bartinelli: $3870; Wong: $4353.75

7. Divide a profit of $7200 between two partners so that the ratio of the shares is 4 to 5. **$3200, $4238**

8. Divide a profit of $18,238 among three partners so that the ratio of the shares is 1:2:3. **$3238, $6238, $9238**

Algebra 1

Enrichment

nth Power Variation

An equation of the form $y = kx^n$, where $k \neq 0$, describes an nth power variation. The variable n can be replaced by 2 to indicate the second power of x (the square of x) or by 3 to indicate the third power of x (the cube of x).

Assume that the weight of a person of average build varies directly as the cube of that person's height. The equation of variation has the form $w = kh^3$.

The weight that a person's legs will support is proportional to the cross-sectional area of the leg bones. This area varies directly as the square of the person's height. The equation of variation has the form $s = kh^2$.

Answer each question.

1. For a person 6 feet tall who weighs 200 pounds, find a value for k in the equation $w = kh^3$.

2. Use your answer from Exercise 1 to predict the weight of a person who is 5 feet tall.

3. Find the value for k in the equation $w = kh^3$ for a baby who is 20 inches long and weighs 6 pounds.

4. How does your answer to Exercise 3 demonstrate that a baby is significantly fatter in proportion to its height than an adult?

5. For a person 6 feet tall who weighs 200 pounds, find a value for k in the equation $s = kh^2$.

6. For a baby who is 20 inches long and weighs 6 pounds, find an "infant value" for k in the equation $s = kh^2$.

7. According to the adult equation you found (Exercise 1), how much would an imaginary giant 20 feet tall weigh?

8. According to the adult equation for weight supported (Exercise 5), how much weight could a 20-foot tall giant's legs actually support?

9. What can you conclude from Exercises 7 and 8?

33

4-8

Enrichment

nth Power Variation

An equation of the form $y = kx^n$, where $k \neq 0$, describes an nth power variation. The variable n can be replaced by 2 to indicate the second power of x (the square of x) or by 3 to indicate the third power of x (the cube of x).

Assume that the weight of a person of average build varies directly as the cube of that person's height. The equation of variation has the form $w = kh^3$.

The weight that a person's legs will support is proportional to the cross-sectional area of the leg bones. This area varies directly as the square of the person's height. The equation of variation has the form $s = kh^2$.

Answer each question.

1. For a person 6 feet tall who weighs 200 pounds, find a value for k in the equation $w = kh^3$. **k = 0.93**

2. Use your answer from Exercise 1 to predict the weight of a person who is 5 feet tall. **about 116 pounds**

3. Find the value for k in the equation $w = kh^3$ for a baby who is 20 inches long and weighs 6 pounds.
k = 1.296 for h = $\frac{5}{3}$ ft

4. How does your answer to Exercise 3 demonstrate that a baby is significantly fatter in proportion to its height than an adult? **k has a greater value.**

5. For a person 6 feet tall who weighs 200 pounds, find a value for k in the equation $s = kh^2$. **k = 5.55**

6. For a baby who is 20 inches long and weighs 6 pounds, find an "infant value" for k in the equation $s = kh^2$.
k = 2.16 for h = $\frac{5}{3}$ ft

7. According to the adult equation you found (Exercise 1), how much would an imaginary giant 20 feet tall weigh?
7440 pounds

8. According to the adult equation for weight supported (Exercise 5), how much weight could a 20-foot tall giant's legs actually support?
only 2222 pounds

9. What can you conclude from Exercises 7 and 8?
Answers will vary. For example, bone strength limits the size humans can attain.

5-1

Enrichment

Coordinate Geometry and Area

How would you find the area of a triangle whose
vertices have the coordinates A $(-1, 2)$, B $(1, 4)$,
and C $(3, 0)$?

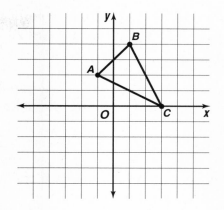

When a figure has no sides parallel to either axis,
the height and base are difficult to find.

One method of finding the area is to enclose the
figure in a rectangle and subtract the area of the
surrounding triangles from the area of the rectangle.

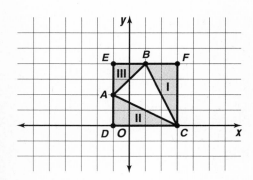

Area of rectangle $DEFC$
$$= 4 \times 4$$
$$= 16 \text{ square units}$$

Area of triangle I $= \frac{1}{2}(2)(4) = 4$

Area of triangle II $= \frac{1}{2}(2)(4) = 4$

Area of triangle III $= \frac{1}{2}(2)(2) = 2$

$$\text{Total} = 10 \text{ square units}$$

Area of triangle $ABC = 16 - 10$,
or 6 square units

Find the areas of the figures with the following vertices.

1. $A(-4, -6)$, $B(0, 4)$,
$C(4, 2)$

2. $A(6, -2)$, $B(8, -10)$,
$C(12, -6)$

3. $A(0, 2)$, $B(2, 7)$,
$C(6, 10)$, $D(9, -2)$

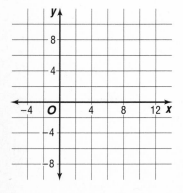

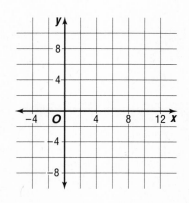

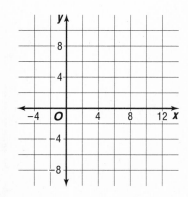

34

Coordinate Geometry and Area

How would you find the area of a triangle whose vertices have the coordinates $A(-1, 2)$, $B(1, 4)$, and $C(3, 0)$?

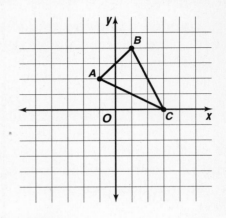

When a figure has no sides parallel to either axis, the height and base are difficult to find.

One method of finding the area is to enclose the figure in a rectangle and subtract the area of the surrounding triangles from the area of the rectangle.

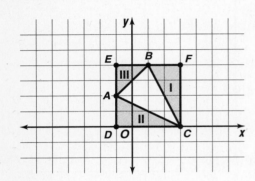

Area of rectangle $DEFC$
$$= 4 \times 4$$
$$= 16 \text{ square units}$$

Area of triangle I $= \frac{1}{2}(2)(4) = 4$

Area of triangle II $= \frac{1}{2}(2)(4) = 4$

Area of triangle III $= \frac{1}{2}(2)(2) = 2$

$\qquad$ Total $= 10$ square units

Area of triangle $ABC = 16 - 10$,
or 6 square units

Find the areas of the figures with the following vertices.

1. $A(-4, -6)$, $B(0, 4)$, $C(4, 2)$
24 square units

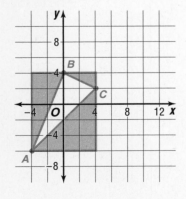

2. $A(6, -2)$, $B(8, -10)$, $C(12, -6)$
20 square units

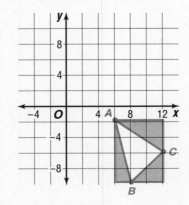

3. $A(0, 2)$, $B(2, 7)$, $C(6, 10)$, $D(9, -2)$
55 square units

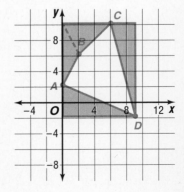

Enrichment

Inverse Relations

On each grid below, plot the points in Sets A and B. Then connect the points in Set A with the corresponding points in Set B. Then find the inverses of Set A and Set B, plot the two sets, and connect those points.

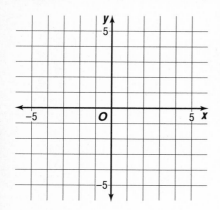

Set A	Set B
(−4, 0)	(0, 1)
(−3, 0)	(0, 2)
(−2, 0)	(0, 3)
(−1, 0)	(0, 4)

Inverse

	Set A	Set B
1.		
2.		
3.		
4.		

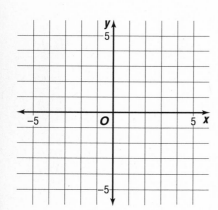

Set A	Set B
(−3, −3)	(−2, 1)
(−2, −2)	(−1, 2)
(−1, −1)	(0, 3)
(0, 0)	(1, 4)

Inverse

	Set A	Set B
5.		
6.		
7.		
8.		

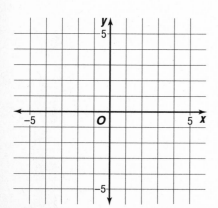

Set A	Set B
(−4, 1)	(3, 2)
(−3, 2)	(3, 2)
(−2, 3)	(3, 2)
(−1, 4)	(3, 2)

Inverse

	Set A	Set B
9.		
10.		
11.		
12.		

13. What is the graphical relationship between the line segments you drew connecting points in Sets A and B and the line segments connecting points in the inverses of those two sets?

NAME_____ DATE _____

Enrichment

Inverse Relations

On each grid below, plot the points in Sets A and B. Then connect the points in Set A with the corresponding points in Set B. Then find the inverses of Set A and Set B, plot the two sets, and connect those points.

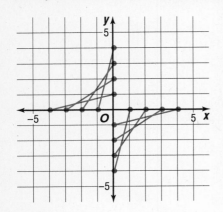

Set A	Set B
(−4, 0)	(0, 1)
(−3, 0)	(0, 2)
(−2, 0)	(0, 3)
(−1, 0)	(0, 4)

Inverse

	Set A	Set B
1.	(0, −4)	(1, 0)
2.	(0, −3)	(2, 0)
3.	(0, −2)	(3, 0)
4.	(0, −1)	(4, 0)

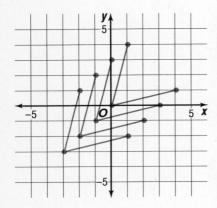

Set A	Set B
(−3, −3)	(−2, 1)
(−2, −2)	(−1, 2)
(−1, −1)	(0, 3)
(0, 0)	(1, 4)

Inverse

	Set A	Set B
5.	(−3, −3)	(1, −2)
6.	(−2, −2)	(2, −1)
7.	(−1, −1)	(3, 0)
8.	(0, 0)	(4, 1)

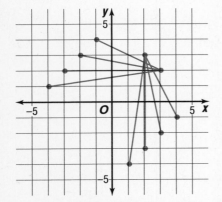

Set A	Set B
(−4, 1)	(3, 2)
(−3, 2)	(3, 2)
(−2, 3)	(3, 2)
(−1, 4)	(3, 2)

Inverse

	Set A	Set B
9.	(1, −4)	(2, 3)
10.	(2, −3)	(2, 3)
11.	(3, −2)	(2, 3)
12.	(4, −1)	(2, 3)

13. What is the graphical relationship between the line segments you drew connecting points in Sets A and B and the line segments connecting points in the inverses of those two sets?
Answers will vary. A possible answer is that the graphs are reflected across the line x = y by their inverses.

Algebra 1

NAME_____ DATE _____

Enrichment

Student Edition
Pages 271–277

Dissection Puzzles: Make the Square

In a dissection puzzle you are to cut apart one figure and then rearrange the pieces to make a new figure. Only straight cuts are allowed. Usually the puzzle-solver must figure out where to make a given number of cuts. However, for these puzzles, the cut lines are shown. You must find out how to rearrange the pieces.

Cut apart the figure shown. Then rearrange the pieces to form a square. Record your solution in the square at the right.

1.

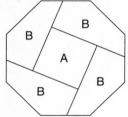

2.

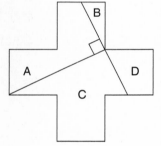

3.

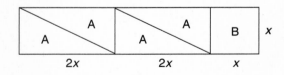

4. For this dissection, you must cut one of the triangles into two pieces to make the square.

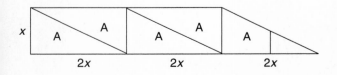

Algebra 1

5-3

Enrichment

Dissection Puzzles: Make the Square

In a dissection puzzle you are to cut apart one figure and then rearrange the pieces to make a new figure. Only straight cuts are allowed. Usually the puzzle-solver must figure out where to make a given number of cuts. However, for these puzzles, the cut lines are shown. You must find out how to rearrange the pieces.

Cut apart the figure shown. Then rearrange the pieces to form a square. Record your solution in the square at the right.

1.
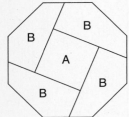
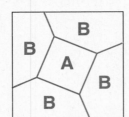

2.
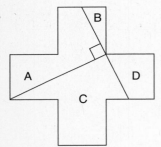
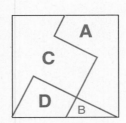

3.
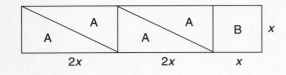
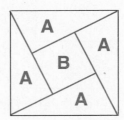

4. For this dissection, you must cut one of the triangles into two pieces to make the square.

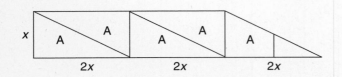
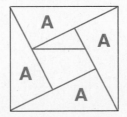

Algebra 1

NAME_____ DATE _____

Enrichment

Taxicab Graphs

You have used a rectangular coordinate system to graph equations such as $y = x - 1$ on a coordinate plane. In a coordinate plane, the numbers in an ordered pair (x, y) can be any two real numbers.

A **taxicab plane** is different from the usual coordinate plane. The only points allowed are those that exist along the horizontal and vertical grid lines. You may think of the points as taxicabs that must stay on the streets.

The taxicab graph shows the equations $y = -2$ and $y = x - 1$. Notice that one of the graphs is no longer a straight line. It is now a collection of separate points.

Taxicab Graph of $y = x - 1$

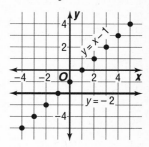

Graph these equations on the taxicab plane at the right.

1. $y = x + 1$ **2.** $y = -2x + 3$

3. $y = 2.5$ **4.** $x = -4$

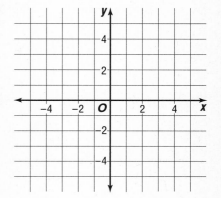

Use your graphs for these problems.

5. Which of the equations would have the same graph in both the usual coordinate plane and the taxicab plane?

6. Describe the form of equations that have the same graph in both the usual coordinate plane and the taxicab plane.

In the taxicab plane, distances are not measured diagonally, but along the streets. Write the taxi-distance between each pair of points.

7. $(0, 0)$ and $(5, 2)$ **8.** $(0, 0)$ and $(-3, 2)$ **9.** $(0, 0)$ and $(2, 1.5)$

10. $(1, 2)$ and $(4, 3)$ **11.** $(2, 4)$ and $(-1, 3)$ **12.** $(0, 4)$ and $(-2, 0)$

Draw these graphs on the taxicab grid at the right.

13. The set of points whose taxi-distance from $(0, 0)$ is 2 units.

14. The set of points whose taxi-distance from $(2, 1)$ is 3 units.

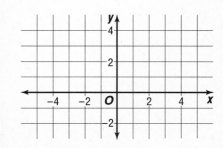

Algebra 1

NAME_____ DATE _____

Enrichment

Taxicab Graphs

You have used a rectangular coordinate system to graph equations such as $y = x - 1$ on a coordinate plane. In a coordinate plane, the numbers in an ordered pair (x, y) can be any two real numbers.

Taxicab Graph of $y = x - 1$

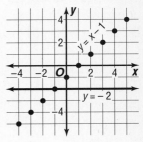

A **taxicab plane** is different from the usual coordinate plane. The only points allowed are those that exist along the horizontal and vertical grid lines. You may think of the points as taxicabs that must stay on the streets.

The taxicab graph shows the equations $y = -2$ and $y = x - 1$. Notice that one of the graphs is no longer a straight line. It is now a collection of separate points.

Graph these equations on the taxicab plane at the right.

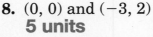 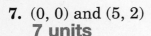

1. $y = x + 1$ **2.** $y = -2x + 3$

3. $y = 2.5$ **4.** $x = -4$

Use your graphs for these problems.

5. Which of the equations would have the same graph in both the usual coordinate plane and the taxicab plane? **$x = -4$**

6. Describe the form of equations that have the same graph in both the usual coordinate plane and the taxicab plane.
$x = A$ and $y = B$, where A and B are integers

In the taxicab plane, distances are not measured diagonally, but along the streets. Write the taxi-distance between each pair of points.

7. $(0, 0)$ and $(5, 2)$
7 units

8. $(0, 0)$ and $(-3, 2)$
5 units

9. $(0, 0)$ and $(2, 1.5)$
3.5 units

10. $(1, 2)$ and $(4, 3)$
4 units

11. $(2, 4)$ and $(-1, 3)$
4 units

12. $(0, 4)$ and $(-2, 0)$
6 units

Draw these graphs on the taxicab grid at the right.

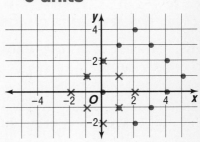

13. The set of points whose taxi-distance from $(0, 0)$ is 2 units. **indicated by crosses**

14. The set of points whose taxi-distance from $(2, 1)$ is 3 units. **indicated by dots**

Enrichment

Composite Functions

Three things are needed to have a function—a set called the *domain,* a set called the *range,* and a *rule* that matches each element in the domain with only one element in the range. Here is an example.

Rule: $f(x) = 2x + 1$

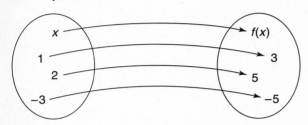

$f(x) = 2x + 1$

$f(1) = 2(1) + 1 = 2 + 1 = 3$

$f(2) = 2(2) + 1 = 4 + 1 = 5$

$f(-3) = 2(-3) + 1 = -6 + 1 = -5$

Suppose we have three sets A, B, and C and two functions described as shown below.

Rule: $f(x) = 2x + 1$ Rule: $g(y) = 3y - 4$

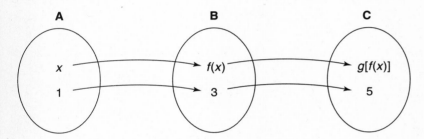

$g(y) = 3y - 4$
$g(3) = 3(3) - 4 = 5$

Let's find a rule that will match elements of set A with elements of set C without finding any elements in set B. In other words, let's find a rule for the **composite function g[f(x)].**

Since $f(x) = 2x + 1$, $g[f(x)] = g(2x + 1)$.
Since $g(y) = 3y - 4$, $g(2x + 1) = 3(2x + 1) - 4$, or $6x - 1$.
Therefore, $g[f(x)] = 6x - 1$.

Find a rule for the composite function g[f(x)].

1. $f(x) = 3x$ and $g(y) = 2y + 1$ **2.** $f(x) = x^2 + 1$ and $g(y) = 4y$

3. $f(x) = -2x$ and $g(y) = y^2 - 3y$ **4.** $f(x) = \dfrac{1}{x - 3}$ and $g(y) = y^{-1}$

5. Is it always the case that $g[f(x)] = f[g(x)]$? Justify your answer.

Algebra 1

Composite Functions

Three things are needed to have a function—a set called the *domain,* a set called the *range,* and a *rule* that matches each element in the domain with only one element in the range. Here is an example.

Rule: $f(x) = 2x + 1$

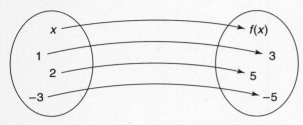

$f(x) = 2x + 1$

$f(1) = 2(1) + 1 = 2 + 1 = 3$

$f(2) = 2(2) + 1 = 4 + 1 = 5$

$f(-3) = 2(-3) + 1 = -6 + 1 = -5$

Suppose we have three sets A, B, and C and two functions described as shown below.

Rule: $f(x) = 2x + 1$ Rule: $g(y) = 3y - 4$

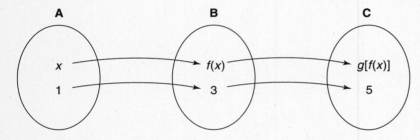

$g(y) = 3y - 4$
$g(3) = 3(3) - 4 = 5$

Let's find a rule that will match elements of set A with elements of set C without finding any elements in set B. In other words, let's find a rule for the **composite function** $g[f(x)]$.

Since $f(x) = 2x + 1, g[f(x)] = g(2x + 1)$.
Since $g(y) = 3y - 4, g(2x + 1) = 3(2x + 1) - 4$, or $6x - 1$.
Therefore, $g[f(x)] = 6x - 1$.

Find a rule for the composite function g[f(x)].

1. $f(x) = 3x$ and $g(y) = 2y + 1$
$g[f(x)] = 6x + 1$

2. $f(x) = x^2 + 1$ and $g(y) = 4y$
$g[f(x)] = 4x^2 + 4$

3. $f(x) = -2x$ and $g(y) = y^2 - 3y$
$g[f(x)] = 4x^2 + 6x$

4. $f(x) = \dfrac{1}{x - 3}$ and $g(y) = y^{-1}$
$g[f(x)] = x - 3$

5. Is it always the case that $g[f(x)] = f[g(x)]$? Justify your answer.
No. For example, in Exercise 1, $f[g(x)] = f(2x + 1) = 3(2x + 1) = 6x + 3$, not $6x + 1$

Algebra 1

NAME_____ DATE _____

Enrichment

Student Edition
Pages 295–302

Polynomial Functions

Suppose a linear equation such as $-3x + y = 4$ is solved for y. Then an equivalent equation, $y = 3x + 4$, is found. Expressed in this way, y is a function of x, or $f(x) = 3x + 4$. Notice that the right side of the equation is a binomial of degree 1.

Higher-degree polynomials in x may also form functions. An example is $f(x) = x^3 + 1$, which is a polynomial function of degree 3. You can graph this function using a table of ordered pairs.

x	y
$-1\frac{1}{2}$	$-2\frac{2}{8}$
-1	0
0	1
1	2
$1\frac{1}{2}$	$4\frac{3}{8}$

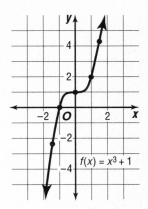

For each of the following polynomial functions, make a table of values for x and y = f(x). Then draw the graph on the grid.

1. $f(x) = 1 - x^2$

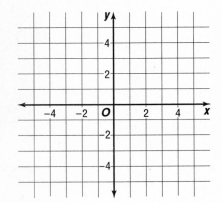

2. $f(x) = x^2 - 5$

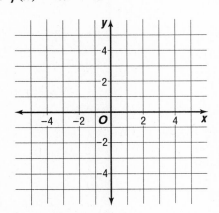

3. $f(x) = x^2 + 4x - 1$

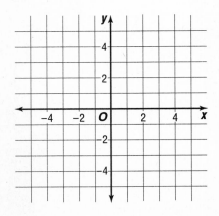

4. $f(x) = x^3$

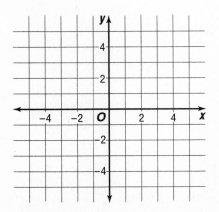

Algebra 1

Polynomial Functions

Suppose a linear equation such as $-3x + y = 4$ is solved for y. Then an equivalent equation, $y = 3x + 4$, is found. Expressed in this way, y is a function of x, or $f(x) = 3x + 4$. Notice that the right side of the equation is a binomial of degree 1.

Higher-degree polynomials in x may also form functions. An example is $f(x) = x^3 + 1$, which is a polynomial function of degree 3. You can graph this function using a table of ordered pairs.

x	y
$-1\frac{1}{2}$	$-2\frac{2}{8}$
-1	0
0	1
1	2
$1\frac{1}{2}$	$4\frac{3}{8}$

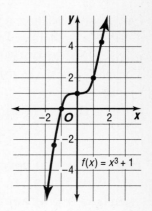

$f(x) = x^3 + 1$

For each of the following polynomial functions, make a table of values for x and y = f(x). Then draw the graph on the grid.

1. $f(x) = 1 - x^2$

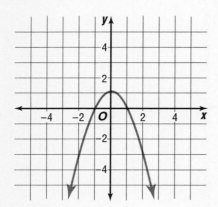

2. $f(x) = x^2 - 5$

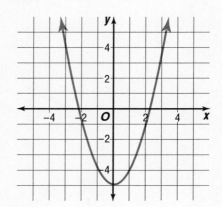

3. $f(x) = x^2 + 4x - 1$

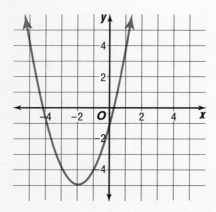

4. $f(x) = x^3$

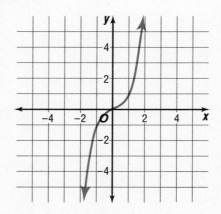

Algebra 1

Standard Deviation

The most commonly used measure of variation is called the
standard deviation. It shows how far the data are from their
mean. You can find the standard deviation using the steps
given below.

a. Find the mean of the data.
b. Find the difference between each value and the mean.
c. Square each difference.
d. Find the mean of the squared differences.
e. Find the square root of the mean found in Step **d.** The result
   is the standard deviation.

Example: Calculate the standard deviation of the test scores
82, 71, 63, 78, and 66.

mean of the data $(m) = \dfrac{82 + 71 + 63 + 78 + 66}{5} = \dfrac{360}{5} = 72$

x	$x - m$	$(x - m)^2$
82	$82 - 72 = 10$	$10^2 = 100$
71	$71 - 72 = -1$	$(-1)^2 = 1$
63	$63 - 72 = -9$	$(-9)^2 = 81$
78	$78 - 72 = 6$	$6^2 = 36$
66	$66 - 72 = -6$	$(-6)^2 = 36$

mean of the squared differences $= \dfrac{100 + 1 + 81 + 36 + 36}{5} = \dfrac{254}{5} = 50.8$

standard deviation $= \sqrt{50.8} \approx 7.13$

**Use the test scores 94, 48, 83, 61, and 74 to complete
Exercises 1-3.**

1. Find the mean of the scores.

2. Show that the standard deviation of the scores is about 16.2.

3. Which had less variations, the test scores listed above or the
   test scores in the example?

5-7

Enrichment

Standard Deviation

The most commonly used measure of variation is called the
standard deviation. It shows how far the data are from their
mean. You can find the standard deviation using the steps
given below.

a. Find the mean of the data.
b. Find the difference between each value and the mean.
c. Square each difference.
d. Find the mean of the squared differences.
e. Find the square root of the mean found in Step **d.** The result
is the standard deviation.

Example: Calculate the standard deviation of the test scores
82, 71, 63, 78, and 66.

mean of the data $(m) = \dfrac{82 + 71 + 63 + 78 + 66}{5} = \dfrac{360}{5} = 72$

x	$x - m$	$(x - m)^2$
82	$82 - 72 = 10$	$10^2 = 100$
71	$71 - 72 = -1$	$(-1)^2 = 1$
63	$63 - 72 = -9$	$(-9)^2 = 81$
78	$78 - 72 = 6$	$6^2 = 36$
66	$66 - 72 = -6$	$(-6)^2 = 36$

mean of the squared differences $= \dfrac{100 + 1 + 81 + 36 + 36}{5} = \dfrac{254}{5} = 50.8$

standard deviation $= \sqrt{50.8} \approx 7.13$

**Use the test scores 94, 48, 83, 61, and 74 to complete
Exercises 1-3.**

1. Find the mean of the scores. **72**

2. Show that the standard deviation of the scores is about 16.2.

x	$x - m$	$(x - m)^2$
94	$94 - 72 = 22$	484
48	$48 - 72 = -24$	576
83	$83 - 72 = 11$	121
61	$61 - 72 = -11$	121
74	$74 - 72 = 2$	4

mean of $(x - m)^2 = 261.2$
S.D. $= \sqrt{261.2} \approx 16.2$

3. Which had less variations, the test scores listed above or the
test scores in the example? **the test scores in the example**

                                                   Algebra 1

Enrichment

Treasure Hunt with Slopes

Using the definition of slope, draw lines with the slopes listed below. A correct solution will trace the route to the treasure.

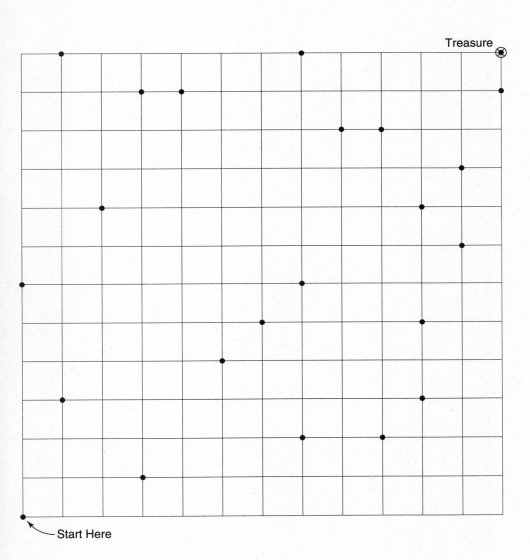

Treasure

Start Here

1. 3

2. $\frac{1}{4}$

3. $-\frac{2}{5}$

4. 0

5. 1

6. -1

7. no slope

8. $\frac{2}{7}$

9. $\frac{3}{2}$

10. $\frac{1}{3}$

11. $-\frac{3}{4}$

12. 3

Algebra 1

Treasure Hunt with Slopes

Using the definition of slope, draw lines with the slopes listed below. A correct solution will trace the route to the treasure.

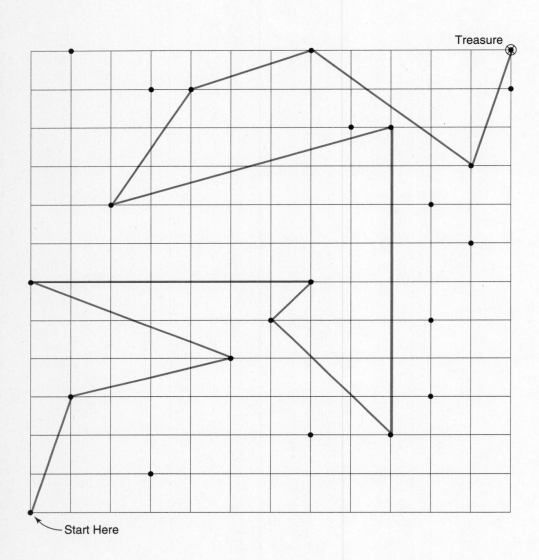

Treasure

Start Here

1. 3

2. $\dfrac{1}{4}$

3. $-\dfrac{2}{5}$

4. 0

5. 1

6. -1

7. no slope

8. $\dfrac{2}{7}$

9. $\dfrac{3}{2}$

10. $\dfrac{1}{3}$

11. $-\dfrac{3}{4}$

12. 3

6-2

Enrichment

Equations of Lines and Planes in Intercept Form

One form that a linear equation may take is **intercept form.** The constants a and b are the x- and y-intercepts of the graph.

$$\frac{x}{a} + \frac{y}{b} = 1$$

In three-dimensional space, the equation of a plane takes a similar form.

$$\frac{x}{a} + \frac{y}{b} + \frac{z}{c} = 1$$

Here, the constants a, b, and c are the points where the plane meets the x, y, and z-axes.

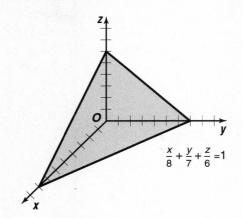

$\frac{x}{8} + \frac{y}{7} + \frac{z}{6} = 1$

Solve each problem.

1. Graph the equation $\frac{x}{3} + \frac{y}{2} + \frac{z}{1} = 1$.

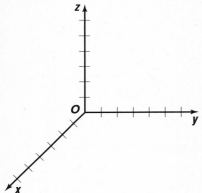

2. For the plane in Exercise 1, write an equation for the line where the plane intersects the xy-plane. Use intercept forms.

3. Write an equation for the line where the plane intersects the xz-plane.

4. Write an equation for the line where the plane intersects the yz-plane.

5. Graph the equation $\frac{x}{1} + \frac{y}{4} + \frac{z}{2} = 1$.

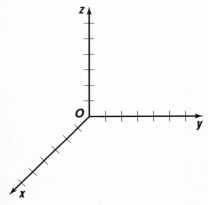

6. Write an equation for the xy-plane.

7. Write an equation for the yz-plane.

8. Write an equation for a plane parallel to the xy-plane with a z-intercept of 2.

9. Write an equation for a plane parallel to the yz-plane with an x-intercept of -3.

Algebra 1

NAME_____ DATE _____

Enrichment

Equations of Lines and Planes in Intercept Form

One form that a linear equation may take is **intercept form.** The constants a and b are the x- and y-intercepts of the graph.

$$\frac{x}{a} + \frac{y}{b} = 1$$

In three-dimensional space, the equation of a plane takes a similar form.

$$\frac{x}{a} + \frac{y}{b} + \frac{z}{c} = 1$$

Here, the constants a, b, and c are the points where the plane meets the x, y, and z-axes.

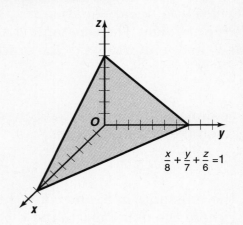

$$\frac{x}{8} + \frac{y}{7} + \frac{z}{6} = 1$$

Solve each problem.

1. Graph the equation $\frac{x}{3} + \frac{y}{2} + \frac{z}{1} = 1$.

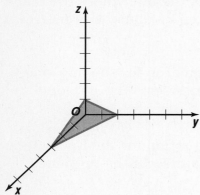

5. Graph the equation $\frac{x}{1} + \frac{y}{4} + \frac{z}{2} = 1$.

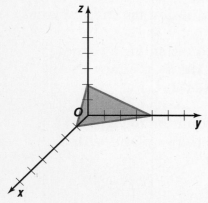

2. For the plane in Exercise 1, write an equation for the line where the plane intersects the xy-plane. Use intercept forms. $\frac{x}{3} + \frac{y}{2} = 1$

3. Write an equation for the line where the plane intersects the xz-plane. $\frac{x}{3} + \frac{z}{1} = 1$

4. Write an equation for the line where the plane intersects the yz-plane. $\frac{y}{2} + \frac{z}{1} = 1$

6. Write an equation for the xy-plane. $z = 0$

7. Write an equation for the yz-plane. $x = 0$

8. Write an equation for a plane parallel to the xy-plane with a z-intercept of 2. $z = 2$

9. Write an equation for a plane parallel to the yz-plane with an x-intercept of -3. $x = -3$

Algebra 1

Enrichment

A Scatter Plot

Each point on the graph shows
the relation between the
number of people attending the
Roxy Cinema and the number
of cars in the parking lot.

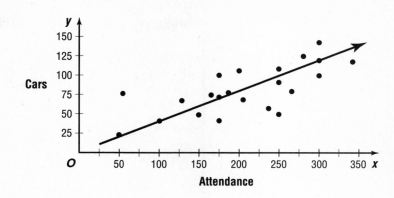

A line is drawn that appears to
lie close to most of the points.
Here is how to find the
equation of this line.

The line passes through (100, 40) and (300, 120). Use the slope-intercept form.

$$m = \frac{120 - 40}{300 - 100}$$

$$= \frac{80}{200}$$

$$= \frac{2}{5}$$

$$y = mx + b$$

$$40 = \frac{2}{5}(100) + b$$

$$0 = b$$

An equation for the line is $y = \frac{2}{5}x$.

Solve each problem.

1. Suppose the owner of the Roxy decides to increase the
seating capacity of the theater to 1000. How many cars
should the parking lot be prepared to accommodate?

2. The points (240, 60) and (340, 120) lie on the scatter plot.
Write an equation for the line through these points.

3. Do you think the equation in Exercise 2 is a good
representation of the relationship in this problem?

4. Suppose the equation for the relationship between
attendance at the theater and cars in the parking lot is
$y = 2x + 20$. What might you suspect about the users of
the parking lot?

A Scatter Plot

Each point on the graph shows the relation between the number of people attending the Roxy Cinema and the number of cars in the parking lot.

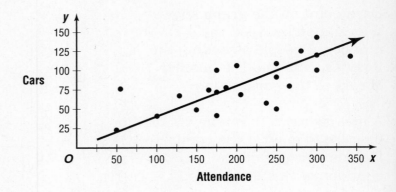

A line is drawn that appears to lie close to most of the points. Here is how to find the equation of this line.

The line passes through (100, 40) and (300, 120). Use the slope-intercept form.

$$m = \frac{120 - 40}{300 - 100}$$

$$= \frac{80}{200}$$

$$= \frac{2}{5}$$

$$y = mx + b$$

$$40 = \frac{2}{5}(100) + b$$

$$0 = b$$

An equation for the line is $y = \frac{2}{5}x$.

Solve each problem.

1. Suppose the owner of the Roxy decides to increase the seating capacity of the theater to 1000. How many cars should the parking lot be prepared to accommodate? **400 cars**

2. The points (240, 60) and (340, 120) lie on the scatter plot. Write an equation for the line through these points. $y = \frac{3}{5}x - 84$

3. Do you think the equation in Exercise 2 is a good representation of the relationship in this problem?
No. The graph of the equation does not appear to go through the center of the data points.

4. Suppose the equation for the relationship between attendance at the theater and cars in the parking lot is $y = 2x + 20$. What might you suspect about the users of the parking lot?
Many people are parking in the lot who are not going to the Roxy.

Enrichment

Analyzing Data

Fill in each table below. Then write _inversely_, or _directly_ to complete each conclusion.

1.

l	2	4	8	16	32
w	4	4	4	4	4
A					

For a set of rectangles with a width of 4, the area varies _____ as the length.

2.

Hours	2	4	5	6
Speed	55	55	55	55
Distance				

For a car traveling at 55 mi/h, the distance covered varies _____ as the hours driven.

3.

Oat bran	$\frac{1}{3}$ cup	$\frac{2}{3}$ cup	1 cup
Water	1 cup	2 cup	3 cup
Servings	1	2	

The number of servings of oat bran varies _____ as the number of cups of oat bran.

4.

Hours of Work	128	128	128
People Working	2	4	8
Hours per Person			

A job requires 128 hours of work. The number of hours each person works varies _____ as the number of people working.

5.

Miles	100	100	100	100
Rate	20	25	50	100
Hours	5			

For a 100-mile car trip, the time the trip takes varies _____ as the average rate of speed the car travels.

6.

b	3	4	5	6
h	10	10	10	10
A	15			

For a set of right triangles with a height of 10, the area varies _____ as the base.

Use the table at the right.

7. x varies _____ as y.

8. z varies _____ as y.

9. x varies _____ as z.

x	1	1.5	2	2.5	3
y	2	3	4	5	6
z	60	40	30	24	20

Algebra 1

6-4

Enrichment

Analyzing Data

Fill in each table below. Then write _inversely_, or _directly_ to complete each conclusion.

1.

l	2	4	8	16	32
w	4	4	4	4	4
A	8	16	32	64	128

For a set of rectangles with a width of 4, the area varies ___directly___ as the length.

2.

Hours	2	4	5	6
Speed	55	55	55	55
Distance	165	220	275	330

For a car traveling at 55 mi/h, the distance covered varies ___directly___ as the hours driven.

3.

Oat bran	$\frac{1}{3}$ cup	$\frac{2}{3}$ cup	1 cup
Water	1 cup	2 cup	3 cup
Servings	1	2	3

The number of servings of oat bran varies ___directly___ as the number of cups of oat bran.

4.

Hours of Work	128	128	128
People Working	2	4	8
Hours per Person	64	32	16

A job requires 128 hours of work. The number of hours each person works varies ___inversely___ as the number of people working.

5.

Miles	100	100	100	100
Rate	20	25	50	100
Hours	5	4	2	1

For a 100-mile car trip, the time the trip takes varies ___inversely___ as the average rate of speed the car travels.

6.

b	3	4	5	6
h	10	10	10	10
A	15	20	25	30

For a set of right triangles with a height of 10, the area varies ___directly___ as the base.

Use the table at the right.

7. x varies ___directly___ as y.

8. z varies ___inversely___ as y.

9. x varies ___inversely___ as z.

x	1	1.5	2	2.5	3
y	2	3	4	5	6
z	60	40	30	24	20

Enrichment

Formulas For a Line

You can think of the slope-intercept form of an equation for a line, $y = mx + b$, as a formula for the line given m and b.

Example: Write the formula for a line given two points (x_1, y_1) and (x_2, y_2).

Use the idea that the slope of a line is the same between any two points.

$$\frac{y - y_1}{x - x_1} = \frac{y_2 - y_1}{x_2 - x_1}$$

Multiply each side by $(x - x_1)$.
$$y - y_1 = \frac{y_2 - y_1}{x_2 - x_1}(x - x_1)$$ *Two-point formula*

If you know two points of a line, you can write an equation for the line directly using this formula.

Use the two-point formula to write an equation for the line that passes through the given points.

1. $(3, 1)$ and $(2, -1)$ **2.** $(-3, 1)$ and $(6, 7)$ **3.** $(-4, 4)$ and $(0, 3)$

4. $(-5, -3)$ and $(7, -3)$ **5.** $(10, 0)$ and $(0, 9)$ **6.** $(a, 0)$ and $(0, b)$

Write the standard form of each equation in Exercises 1–6.

7. Exercise 1   **8.** Exercise 2   **9.** Exercise 3

10. Exercise 4   **11.** Exercise 5   **12.** Exercise 6

Solve each problem.

13. Write a formula for an equation of a line given x-intercept a and y-intercept b.

14. Write a formula for an equation of a line given the slope m and one point (x_1, y_1).

Enrichment

Formulas For a Line

You can think of the slope-intercept form of an equation for a line, $y = mx + b$, as a formula for the line given m and b.

Example: Write the formula for a line given two points (x_1, y_1) and (x_2, y_2).

Use the idea that the slope of a line is the same between any two points.

$$\frac{y - y_1}{x - x_1} = \frac{y_2 - y_1}{x_2 - x_1}$$

Multiply each side by $(x - x_1)$.

$$y - y_1 = \frac{y_2 - y_1}{x_2 - x_1}(x - x_1)$$

Two-point formula

If you know two points of a line, you can write an equation for the line directly using this formula.

Use the two-point formula to write an equation for the line that passes through the given points. After exercise 1, only one of the two answers is given.

1. $(3, 1)$ and $(2, -1)$
$$y - 1 = 2(x - 3),$$
$$y + 1 = 2(x - 2)$$

2. $(-3, 1)$ and $(6, 7)$
$$y - 1 = \frac{2}{3}(x + 3)$$

3. $(-4, 4)$ and $(0, 3)$
$$y - 4 = -\frac{1}{4}(x + 4)$$

4. $(-5, -3)$ and $(7, -3)$
$$y = -3$$

5. $(10, 0)$ and $(0, 9)$
$$y = -\frac{9}{10}(x - 10)$$

6. $(a, 0)$ and $(0, b)$
$$y = -\frac{b}{a}(x - a)$$

Write the standard form of each equation in Exercises 1–6.

7. Exercise 1
$$2x - y = 5$$

8. Exercise 2
$$2x - 3y = -9$$

9. Exercise 3
$$x + 4y = 12$$

10. Exercise 4
$$y = -3$$

11. Exercise 5
$$9x + 10y = 90$$

12. Exercise 6
$$bx + ay = ab$$

Solve each problem.

13. Write a formula for an equation of a line given x-intercept a and y-intercept b.
$$bx + ay = ab, \text{ or } \frac{x}{a} + \frac{y}{b} = 1$$

14. Write a formula for an equation of a line given the slope m and one point (x_1, y_1).
$$y - y_1 = m(x - x_1)$$
$$\text{or } mx - y = mx_1 - y_1$$

Enrichment

Pencils of Lines

All of the lines that pass through a single point in the same plane are called a **pencil of lines.**

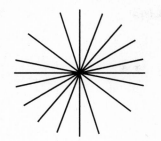
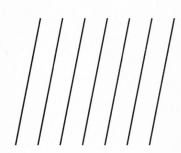

All lines with the same slope, but different intercepts, are also called a "pencil," a **pencil of parallel lines.**

Graph some of the lines in each pencil.

1. A pencil of lines through the point (1, 3)

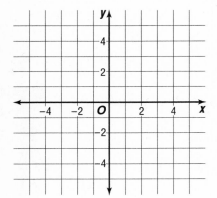

2. A pencil of lines described by $y - 4 = m(x - 2)$, where m is any real number

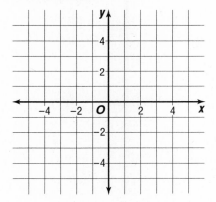

3. A pencil of lines parallel to the line $x - 2y = 7$

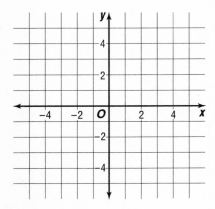

4. A pencil of lines described by $y = mx + 3m - 2$

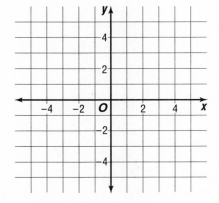

Algebra 1

NAME_____ DATE _____

Enrichment

Pencils of Lines

All of the lines that pass through a single point in the same plane are called a **pencil of lines.**

All lines with the same slope, but different intercepts, are also called a "pencil," a **pencil of parallel lines.**

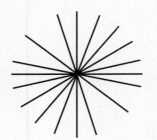

Graph some of the lines in each pencil.

1. A pencil of lines through the point (1, 3)

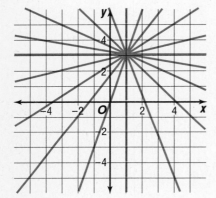

2. A pencil of lines described by $y - 4 = m(x - 2)$, where m is any real number

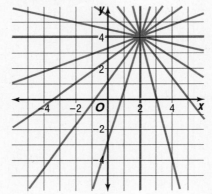

3. A pencil of lines parallel to the line $x - 2y = 7$

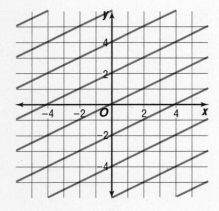

4. A pencil of lines described by $y = mx + 3m - 2$

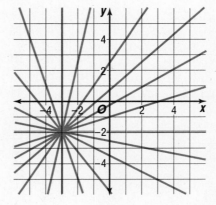

   Algebra 1

NAME_____ DATE _____

Enrichment

Celsius and Kelvin Temperatures

If you blow up a balloon and put it in the refrigerator, the balloon will shrink as the temperature of the air in the balloon decreases.

The volume of a certain gas is measured at 30° Celsius. The temperature is decreased and the volume is measured again.

Temperature (t)	Volume (v)
30°C	202 mL
21°C	196 mL
0°C	182 mL
−12°C	174 mL
−27°C	164 mL

1. Graph this table on the coordinate plane provided below.

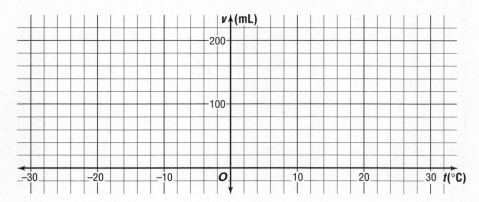

2. Find the equation of the line that passes through the points you graphed in Exercise 1.

3. Use the equation you found in Exercise 2 to find the temperature that would give a volume of zero. This temperature is the lowest one possible and is called "absolute zero."

4. In 1848 Lord Kelvin proposed a new temperature scale with 0 being assigned to absolute zero. The size of the degree chosen was the same size as the Celsius degree. Change each of the Celsius temperatures in the table above to degrees Kelvin.

Enrichment

Celsius and Kelvin Temperatures

If you blow up a balloon and put it in the refrigerator, the balloon will shrink as the temperature of the air in the balloon decreases.

The volume of a certain gas is measured at 30° Celsius. The temperature is decreased and the volume is measured again.

Temperature (t)	Volume (v)
30°C	202 mL
21°C	196 mL
0°C	182 mL
−12°C	174 mL
−27°C	164 mL

1. Graph this table on the coordinate plane provided below.

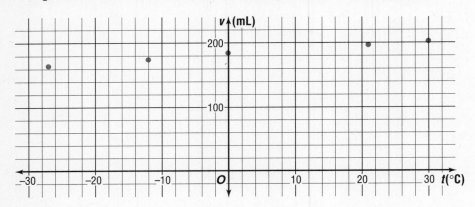

2. Find the equation of the line that passes through the points you graphed in Exercise 1. $y = \frac{2}{3}x + 182$ or $v = \frac{2}{3}t + 182$

3. Use the equation you found in Exercise 2 to find the temperature that would give a volume of zero. This temperature is the lowest one possible and is called "absolute zero." −273°C

4. In 1848 Lord Kelvin proposed a new temperature scale with 0 being assigned to absolute zero. The size of the degree chosen was the same size as the Celsius degree. Change each of the Celsius temperatures in the table above to degrees Kelvin. 303°, 294°, 273°, 261°, 246°

Inequalities with Triangles

Recall that a line segment can be named by the letters of its
endpoints. Line segment AB (written as "$\overline{AB}$") has points A and B
for endpoints. The *length* of AB is written without the bar as AB.

$$AB < BC \qquad\qquad \angle A < \angle B$$

The statement on the left above shows that $\overline{AB}$ is shorter than
$\overline{BC}$. The statement on the right above shows that the measure
of angle A is less than that of angle B.

These three inequalities are true for any triangle
ABC, no matter how long the sides are.

a. $AB + BC > AC$
b. If $AB > AC$, then $\angle C > \angle B$.
c. If $\angle C > \angle B$, then $AB > AC$.

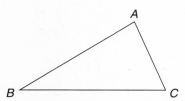

Use the three triangle inequalities for these problems.

1. List the sides of triangle DEF in order
of increasing length.

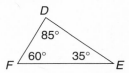

2. In the figure below, which line segment
is the shortest?

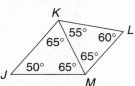

3. Explain why the lengths 5 cm, 10 cm,
and 20 cm could not be used to make a
triangle.

4. Two sides of a triangle measure 3 in.
and 7 in. Between which two values
must the third side be?

5. In triangle XYZ, XY = 15, YZ = 12, and XZ = 9. Which is
the greatest angle? Which is the least?

6. List the angles $\angle A$, $\angle C$, $\angle ABC$, and $\angle ABD$, in order
of increasing size.

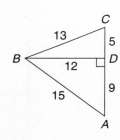

Enrichment

Inequalities with Triangles

Recall that a line segment can be named by the letters of its endpoints. Line segment AB (written as "$\overline{AB}$") has points A and B for endpoints. The *length* of AB is written without the bar as AB.

$$AB < BC \qquad\qquad \angle A < \angle B$$

The statement on the left above shows that $\overline{AB}$ is shorter than $\overline{BC}$. The statement on the right above shows that the measure of angle A is less than that of angle B.

These three inequalities are true for any triangle ABC, no matter how long the sides are.

a. $AB + BC > AC$
b. If $AB > AC$, then $\angle C > \angle B$.
c. If $\angle C > \angle B$, then $AB > AC$.

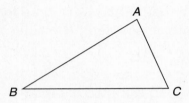

Use the three triangle inequalities for these problems.

1. List the sides of triangle DEF in order of increasing length.
$\overline{DF}, \overline{DE}, \overline{EF}$

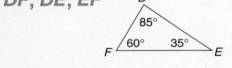

2. In the figure below, which line segment is the shortest?
$\overline{LM}$

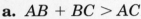

3. Explain why the lengths 5 cm, 10 cm, and 20 cm could not be used to make a triangle. **5 + 10 is not greater than 20.**

4. Two sides of a triangle measure 3 in. and 7 in. Between which two values must the third side be? **4 in. and 10 in.**

5. In triangle XYZ, $XY = 15$, $YZ = 12$, and $XZ = 9$. Which is the greatest angle? Which is the least?
$\angle Z$; $\angle Y$

6. List the angles $\angle A$, $\angle C$, $\angle ABC$, and $\angle ABD$, in order of increasing size.
$\angle ABD$, $\angle A$, $\angle ABC$, $\angle C$

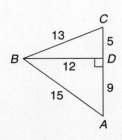

Traceable Figures

Try to trace over each of the figures below without tracing the same segment twice.

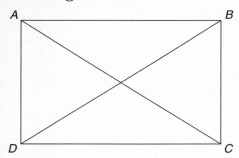

The figure at the left cannot be traced, but the one at the right can. The rule is that a figure is traceable if it has no points, or exactly two points where an odd number of segments meet. The figure at the left has three segments meeting at each of the four corners. However, the figure at the right has exactly two points, L and Q, where an odd number of segments meet.

Determine whether each figure can be traced. If it can, then name the starting point and number the sides in the order in which they should be traced.

1.

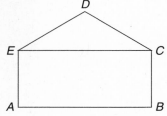

2.

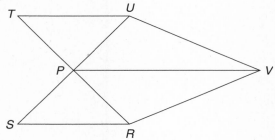

3.

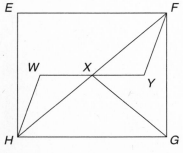

4.

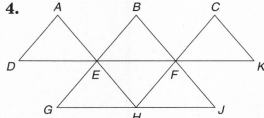

Enrichment

Traceable Figures

Try to trace over each of the figures below without tracing the
same segment twice.

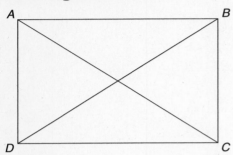

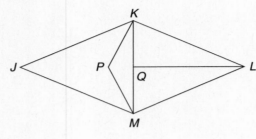

The figure at the left cannot be traced, but the one at the right
can. The rule is that a figure is traceable if it has no points, or
exactly two points where an odd number of segments meet. The
figure at the left has three segments meeting at each of the four
corners. However, the figure at the right has exactly two points,
L and *Q*, where an odd number of segments meet.

**Determine whether each figure can be traced. If it can, then
name the starting point and number the sides in the order in
which they should be traced.**

1.   **Yes E**

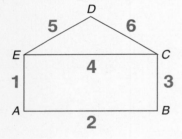

2.   **No**

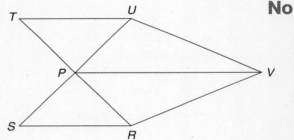

3.   **Yes X**

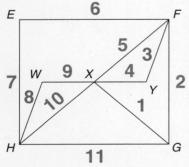

4.   **Yes D**

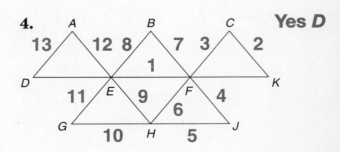

Student Edition
Pages 399–404

Enrichment

Some Properties of Inequalities

The two expressions on either side of an inequality symbol are sometimes called the *first* and *second* members of the inequality.

If the inequality symbols of two inequalities point in the same direction, the inequalities have the same sense. For example, $a < b$ and $c < d$ have the same sense; $a < b$ and $c > d$ have opposite senses.

In the problems on this page, you will explore some properties of inequalities.

Three of the four statements below are true for all numbers a and b (or a, b, c, and d). Write each statement in algebraic form. If the statement is true for all numbers, prove it. If it is not true, give an example to show that it is false.

1. Given an inequality, a new and equivalent inequality can be created by interchanging the members and reversing the sense.

2. Given an inequality, a new and equivalent inequality can be created by changing the signs of both terms and reversing the sense.

3. Given two inequalities with the same sense, the sum of the corresponding members are members of an equivalent inequality with the same sense.

4. Given two inequalities with the same sense, the difference of the corresponding members are members of an equivalent inequality with the same sense.

Enrichment

Some Properties of Inequalities

The two expressions on either side of an inequality symbol are sometimes called the *first* and *second* members of the inequality.

If the inequality symbols of two inequalities point in the same direction, the inequalities have the same sense. For example, $a < b$ and $c < d$ have the same sense; $a < b$ and $c > d$ have opposite senses.

In the problems on this page, you will explore some properties of inequalities.

Three of the four statements below are true for all numbers a and b (or a, b, c, and d). Write each statement in algebraic form. If the statement is true for all numbers, prove it. If it is not true, give an example to show that it is false.

1. Given an inequality, a new and equivalent inequality can be created by interchanging the members and reversing the sense.
   If $a > b$, then $b < a$.
   $a > b$, $a - b > 0$, $-b > -a$, $(-1)(-b) < (-1)(-a)$, $b < a$

2. Given an inequality, a new and equivalent inequality can be created by changing the signs of both terms and reversing the sense.
   If $a > b$, then $-a < -b$.
   $a > b$, $a - b > 0$, $-b > -a$, $-a < -b$

3. Given two inequalities with the same sense, the sum of the corresponding members are members of an equivalent inequality with the same sense.
   If $a > b$ and $c > d$, then $a + c > b + d$.
   $a > b$ and $c > d$, so $(a - b)$ and $(c - d)$ are positive numbers, so the sum $(a - b) + (c - d)$ is also positive.
   $a - b + c - d > 0$, so $a + c > b + d$.

4. Given two inequalities with the same sense, the difference of the corresponding members are members of an equivalent inequality with the same sense.
   If $a > b$ and $c > d$, then $a - c > b - d$. The statement is false. $5 > 4$ and $3 > 2$, but $5 - 3 \not> 4 - 2$.

Enrichment

Precision of Measurement

The precision of a measurement depends both on your accuracy in measuring and the number of divisions on the ruler you use. Suppose you measured a length of wood to the nearest one-eighth of an inch and got a length of $6\frac{5}{8}$ in.

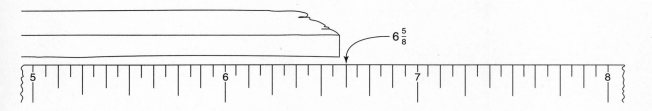

The drawing shows that the actual measurement lies somewhere between $6\frac{9}{16}$ in. and $6\frac{11}{16}$ in. This measurement can be written using the symbol $\pm$, which is read "plus or minus." It can also be written as a compound inequality.

$$6\frac{5}{8} \pm \frac{1}{16} \text{ in.} \qquad\qquad 6\frac{9}{16} \text{ in.} \le m \le 6\frac{11}{16} \text{ in.}$$

In this example, $\frac{1}{16}$ in. is the absolute error. The absolute error is one-half the smallest unit used in a measurement.

Write each measurement as a compound inequality. Use the variable m.

1. $3\frac{1}{2} \pm \frac{1}{4}$ in.

2. 9.78 ± 0.005 cm

3. 2.4 ± 0.05 g

4. $28 \pm \frac{1}{2}$ ft

5. 15 ± 0.5 cm

6. $\frac{11}{16} \pm \frac{1}{64}$ in.

For each measurement, give the smallest unit used and the absolute error.

7. $12.5 \text{ cm} \le m \le 13.5 \text{ cm}$

8. $12\frac{1}{8} \text{ in.} \le m \le 12\frac{3}{8} \text{ in.}$

9. $56\frac{1}{2} \text{ in.} \le m \le 57\frac{1}{2} \text{ in.}$

10. $23.05 \text{ mm} \le m \le 23.15 \text{ mm}$

Enrichment

Precision of Measurement

The precision of a measurement depends both on your accuracy in measuring and the number of divisions on the ruler you use. Suppose you measured a length of wood to the nearest one-eighth of an inch and got a length of $6\frac{5}{8}$ in.

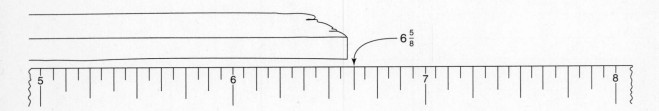

The drawing shows that the actual measurement lies somewhere between $6\frac{9}{16}$ in. and $6\frac{11}{16}$ in. This measurement can be written using the symbol $\pm$, which is read "plus or minus." It can also be written as a compound inequality.

$$6\frac{5}{8} \pm \frac{1}{16} \text{ in.} \qquad\qquad 6\frac{9}{16} \text{ in.} \le m \le 6\frac{11}{16} \text{ in.}$$

In this example, $\frac{1}{16}$ in. is the absolute error. The absolute error is one-half the smallest unit used in a measurement.

Write each measurement as a compound inequality. Use the variable m.

1. $3\frac{1}{2} \pm \frac{1}{4}$ in.

$3\frac{1}{4}$ in. $\le m \le 3\frac{3}{4}$ in.

2. 9.78 ± 0.005 cm

9.775 cm $\le m \le$ **9.785 cm**

3. 2.4 ± 0.05 g

2.35 g $\le m \le$ **2.45 g**

4. $28 \pm \frac{1}{2}$ ft

$27\frac{1}{2}$ **ft** $\le m \le 28\frac{1}{2}$ **ft**

5. 15 ± 0.5 cm

14.5 cm $\le m \le$ **15.5 cm**

6. $\frac{11}{16} \pm \frac{1}{64}$ in.

$\frac{43}{64}$ **in.** $\le m \le \frac{45}{64}$ **in.**

For each measurement, give the smallest unit used and the absolute error.

7. 12.5 cm $\le m \le 13.5$ cm

1 cm, 0.5 cm

8. $12\frac{1}{8}$ in. $\le m \le 12\frac{3}{8}$ in.

$\frac{1}{4}$ **in.,** $\frac{1}{8}$ **in.**

9. $56\frac{1}{2}$ in. $\le m \le 57\frac{1}{2}$ in.

1 in., $\frac{1}{2}$ **in.**

10. 23.05 mm $\le m \le 23.15$ mm

0.1 mm, 0.05 mm

Enrichment

Conditional Probability

The probability of an event given the occurrence of another event is called **conditional probability.** The conditional probability of event A given event B is denoted $P(A|B)$.

Example: Suppose a pair of number cubes is rolled. It is known that the sum is greater than seven. Find the probability that the number cubes match.

There are 15 sums greater than seven and there are 36 possible pairs altogether.

There are three matching pairs greater than seven, $(4, 4)$, $(5, 5)$, and $(6, 6)$.

$$P(B) = \frac{15}{36}$$

$$P(A \text{ and } B) = \frac{3}{36}$$

$$P(A|B) = \frac{P(A \text{ and } B)}{P(B)}$$

$$= \frac{\frac{3}{36}}{\frac{15}{36}} \text{ or } \frac{1}{5}$$

The conditional probability is $\frac{1}{5}$.

A card is drawn from a standard deck of 52 cards and is found to be red. Given that event, find each of the following probabilities.

1. $P(\text{heart})$

2. $P(\text{ace})$

3. $P(\text{face card})$

4. $P(\text{jack or ten})$

5. $P(\text{six of spades})$

6. $P(\text{six of hearts})$

A sports survey taken at Stirers High School shows that 48% of the respondents liked soccer, 66% liked basketball, and 38% liked hockey. Also, 30% liked soccer and basketball, 22% liked basketball and hockey and 28% liked soccer and hockey. Finally, 12% liked all three sports.

7. Find the probability that Meg likes soccer if she likes basketball.

8. Find the probability that Juan likes basketball if he likes soccer.

9. Find the probability that Mieko likes hockey if she likes basketball.

10. Find the probability that Greg likes hockey if he likes soccer.

NAME_____ DATE _____

Enrichment

Conditional Probability

The probability of an event given the occurrence of another event is called **conditional probability.** The conditional probability of event A given event B is denoted $P(A|B)$.

Example: Suppose a pair of number cubes is rolled. It is known that the sum is greater than seven. Find the probability that the number cubes match.

There are 15 sums greater than seven and there are 36 possible pairs altogether.

$$P(B) = \frac{15}{36}$$

There are three matching pairs greater than seven, $(4, 4)$, $(5, 5)$, and $(6, 6)$.

$$P(A \text{ and } B) = \frac{3}{36}$$

$$P(A|B) = \frac{P(A \text{ and } B)}{P(B)}$$

$$= \frac{\frac{3}{36}}{\frac{15}{36}} \text{ or } \frac{1}{5}$$

The conditional probability is $\frac{1}{5}$.

A card is drawn from a standard deck of 52 cards and is found to be red. Given that event, find each of the following probabilities.

1. P(heart) $\frac{1}{2}$

2. P(ace) $\frac{1}{13}$

3. P(face card) $\frac{3}{13}$

4. P(jack or ten) $\frac{2}{13}$

5. P(six of spades) **0**

6. P(six of hearts) $\frac{1}{26}$

A sports survey taken at Stirers High School shows that 48% of the respondents liked soccer, 66% liked basketball, and 38% liked hockey. Also, 30% liked soccer and basketball, 22% liked basketball and hockey and 28% liked soccer and hockey. Finally, 12% liked all three sports.

7. Find the probability that Meg likes soccer if she likes basketball. $\frac{5}{11}$

8. Find the probability that Juan likes basketball if he likes soccer. $\frac{5}{8}$

9. Find the probability that Mieko likes hockey if she likes basketball. $\frac{1}{3}$

10. Find the probability that Greg likes hockey if he likes soccer. $\frac{7}{12}$

Consecutive Integer Problems

Many types of problems and puzzles involve the idea of consecutive integers. Here is an example.

Find four consecutive odd integers whose sum is -80.

An odd integer can be written as $2n + 1$, where n is any of the numbers 0, 1, 2, 3, and so on. Then, the equation for the problem is as follows.

$$(2n + 1) + (2n + 3) + (2n + 5) + (2n + 7) = -80$$

Solve these problems. Write an equation or inequality for each.

1. Complete the solution to the problem in the example.

2. Find three consecutive even integers whose sum is 132.

3. Find the two least consecutive integers whose sum is greater than 20.

4. Find the two greatest consecutive integers whose sum is less than 100.

5. The lesser of two consecutive even integers is 10 more than one-half the greater. Find the integers.

6. The greater of two consecutive even integers is 6 less than three times the lesser. Find the integers.

7. Find four consecutive integers such that twice the sum of the two greater integers exceeds three times the first by 91.

8. Find all sets of four consecutive positive integers such that the greatest integer in the set is greater than twice the least integer in the set.

Enrichment

Consecutive Integer Problems

Many types of problems and puzzles involve the idea of consecutive integers. Here is an example.

Find four consecutive odd integers whose sum is -80.

An odd integer can be written as $2n + 1$, where n is any of the numbers 0, 1, 2, 3, and so on. Then, the equation for the problem is as follows.

$$(2n + 1) + (2n + 3) + (2n + 5) + (2n + 7) = -80$$

Solve these problems. Write an equation or inequality for each.

1. Complete the solution to the problem in the example.
$n = -12$; The integers are -23, -21, -19, -17.

2. Find three consecutive even integers whose sum is 132.
$2n + (2n + 2) + (2n + 4) = 132$; $n = 21$; Integers are 42, 44, 46.

3. Find the two least consecutive integers whose sum is greater than 20.
$n + (n + 1) > 20$; $n > 9.5$; Integers are 10 and 11.

4. Find the two greatest consecutive integers whose sum is less than 100.
$n + (n + 1) < 100$; $n < 49.5$; Integers are 49 and 50.

5. The lesser of two consecutive even integers is 10 more than one-half the greater. Find the integers.
$2n = 10 + \frac{1}{2}(2n + 2$; $n = 11$; Integers are 22 and 24.

6. The greater of two consecutive even integers is 6 less than three times the lesser. Find the integers.
$2n + 2 = 3(2n) - 6$; $n = 2$; Integers are 4 and 6.

7. Find four consecutive integers such that twice the sum of the two greater integers exceeds three times the first by 91.
$2[(n + 2) + (n + 3)] = 3n + 91$; $n = 81$; Integers are 81, 82, 83, 84.

8. Find all sets of four consecutive positive integers such that the greatest integer in the set is greater than twice the least integer in the set.
$n + 3 > 2n$; $n < 3$; The two sets are $\{1, 2, 3, 4\}$ and $\{2, 3, 4, 5\}$.

NAME_____ DATE _____

Enrichment

Curious Circles

Two circles can be arranged in four ways: one circle can be inside the other, they can be separate, they can overlap, or they can coincide.

In how many ways can a given number of circles be either separate or inside each other? (The situations in which the circles overlap or coincide are not counted here.)

Here is the answer for 3 circles. There are 4 different possibilities.

1   2   3    4

Solve each problem. Make drawings to show your answers.

1. Show the different ways in which 2 circles can be separate or inside each other. How many ways are there?

2. Show the different ways for 4 circles. How many ways are there?

3. Use your answer for Exercise 2 to show that the number of ways for 5 circles is at least 18.

4. Find the number of ways for 5 circles. Show your drawings on a separate sheet of paper.

NAME _____ DATE _____

Enrichment

Curious Circles

Two circles can be arranged in four ways: one circle can be inside the other, they can be separate, they can overlap, or they can coincide.

In how many ways can a given number of circles be either separate or inside each other? (The situations in which the circles overlap or coincide are not counted here.)

Here is the answer for 3 circles. There are 4 different possibilities.

Solve each problem. Make drawings to show your answers.

1. Show the different ways in which 2 circles can be separate or inside each other. How many ways are there? **two ways**

2. Show the different ways for 4 circles. How many ways are there?
   nine ways

 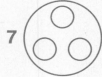 

3. Use your answer for Exercise 2 to show that the number of ways for 5 circles is at least 18. **see below**

4. Find the number of ways for 5 circles. Show your drawings on a separate sheet of paper. **20 ways**

3. First, draw an extra circle next to each of the ways for 4 circles. Then draw a circle around each of the ways for 4 circles.

Algebra 1

Enrichment

Absolute Value Functions

Some types of functions that occur frequently have special names. Absolute value functions are an example.

Example: Graph $y = |x + 2|$.

x	y
−4	2
−3	1
−2	0
−1	1
0	2
1	3
2	4

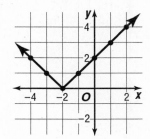

Complete the table for each equation. Then, draw the graph.

1. $y = |x|$

x	y
−3	
−2	
−1	
0	
1	
2	
3	

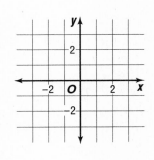

2. $y = |x| - 2$

x	y
−3	
−2	
−1	
0	
1	
2	
3	

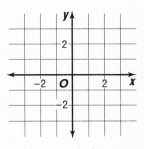

3. $y = |x - 1|$

x	y
−2	
−1	
0	
1	
2	
3	
4	

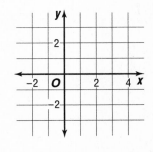

4. $y = |2 - x|$

x	y
−2	
−1	
0	
1	
2	
3	
4	

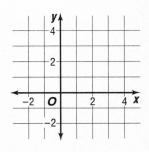

Enrichment

Absolute Value Functions

Some types of functions that occur frequently have special names. Absolute value functions are an example.

Example: Graph $y = |x + 2|$.

x	y
−4	2
−3	1
−2	0
−1	1
0	2
1	3
2	4

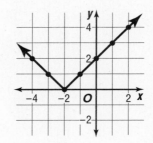

Complete the table for each equation. Then, draw the graph.

1. $y = |x|$

x	y
−3	3
−2	2
−1	1
0	0
1	1
2	2
3	3

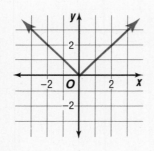

2. $y = |x| - 2$

x	y
−3	1
−2	0
−1	−1
0	−2
1	−1
2	0
3	1

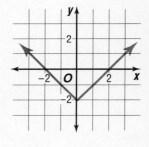

3. $y = |x - 1|$

x	y
−2	3
−1	2
0	1
1	0
2	1
3	2
4	3

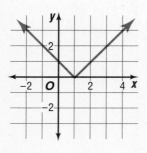

4. $y = |2 - x|$

x	y
−2	4
−1	3
0	2
1	1
2	0
3	1
4	2

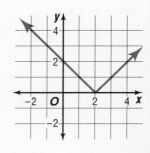

 Algebra 1

Enrichment

Graphing a Trip

The distance formula, $d = rt$, is used to solve many types of problems. If you graph an equation such as $d = 50t$, the graph is a model for a car going at 50 mi/h. The time the car travels is t; the distance in miles the car covers is d. The slope of the line is the speed.

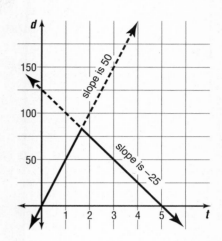

Suppose you drive to a nearby town and return. You average 50 mi/h on the trip out but only 25 mi/h on the trip home. The round trip takes 5 hours. How far away is the town?

The graph at the right represents your trip. Notice that the return trip is shown with a negative slope because you are driving in the opposite direction.

Solve each problem.

1. Estimate the answer to the problem in the above example. About how far away is the town?

2. Graph this trip and solve the problem. An airplane has enough fuel for 3 hours of safe flying. On the trip out the pilot averages 200 mi/h flying against a headwind. On the trip back, the pilot averages 250 mi/h. How long a trip out can the pilot make?

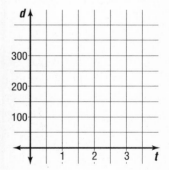

3. Graph this trip and solve the problem. You drive to a town 100 miles away. On the trip out you average 25 mi/h. On the trip back you average 50 mi/h. How many hours do you spend driving?

4. Graph this trip and solve the problem. You drive at an average speed of 50 mi/h to a discount shopping plaza, spend 2 hours shopping, and then return at an average speed of 25 mi/h. The entire trip takes 8 hours. How far away is the shopping plaza?

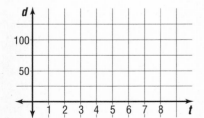

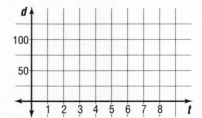

56

NAME_____ DATE _____

Enrichment

Graphing a Trip

The distance formula, $d = rt$, is used to solve many types of problems. If you graph an equation such as $d = 50t$, the graph is a model for a car going at 50 mi/h. The time the car travels is t; the distance in miles the car covers is d. The slope of the line is the speed.

Suppose you drive to a nearby town and return. You average 50 mi/h on the trip out but only 25 mi/h on the trip home. The round trip takes 5 hours. How far away is the town?

The graph at the right represents your trip. Notice that the return trip is shown with a negative slope because you are driving in the opposite direction.

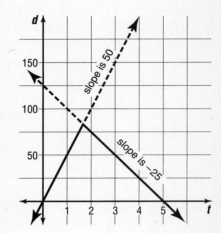

Solve each problem.

1. Estimate the answer to the problem in the above example. About how far away is the town?
   about 80 miles

2. Graph this trip and solve the problem. An airplane has enough fuel for 3 hours of safe flying. On the trip out the pilot averages 200 mi/h flying against a headwind. On the trip back, the pilot averages 250 mi/h. How long a trip out can the pilot make?

   about $1\frac{2}{3}$ hours and 330 miles

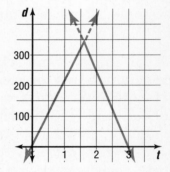

3. Graph this trip and solve the problem. You drive to a town 100 miles away. On the trip out you average 25 mi/h. On the trip back you average 50 mi/h. How many hours do you spend driving?
   6 hours

4. Graph this trip and solve the problem. You drive at an average speed of 50 mi/h to a discount shopping plaza, spend 2 hours shopping, and then return at an average speed of 25 mi/h. The entire trip takes 8 hours. How far away is the shopping plaza? **100 miles**

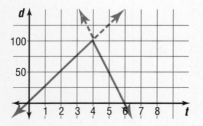

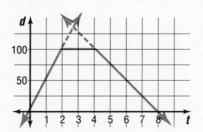

T56

Enrichment

Using Equations: Ideal Weight

You can find your ideal weight as follows.
A woman should weigh 100 pounds for the first 5 feet of height and 5 additional pounds for each inch over 5 feet (5 feet = 60 inches). A man should weigh 106 pounds for the first 5 feet of height and 6 additional pounds for each inch over 5 feet. These formulas apply to people with normal bone structures.

To determine your bone structure, wrap your thumb and index finger around the wrist of your other hand. If the thumb and finger just touch, you have normal bone structure. If they overlap, you are small-boned. If they don't overlap, you are large-boned. Small-boned people should decrease their calculated ideal weight by 10%. Large-boned people should increase the value by 10%.

Calculate the ideal weights of these people.

1. woman, 5 ft 4 in., normal-boned

2. man, 5 ft 11 in., large-boned

3. man, 6 ft 5 in., small-boned

4. you, if you are at least 5 ft tall

Suppose a normal-boned man is x inches tall. If he is at least 5 feet tall, then x − 60 represents the number of inches this man is over 5 feet tall. For each of these inches, his ideal weight is increased by 6 pounds. Thus, his proper weight (y) is given by the formula y = 6(x − 60) + 106 or y = 6x − 254. If the man is large-boned, the formula becomes y = 6x − 254 + 0.10(6x − 254).

5. Write the formula for the weight of a large-boned man in slope-intercept form.

6. Derive the formula for the ideal weight (y) of a normal-boned female with height x inches. Write the formula in slope-intercept form.

7. Derive the formula in slope-intercept form for the ideal weight (y) of a large-boned female with height x inches.

8. Derive the formula in slope-intercept form for the ideal weight (y) of a small-boned male with height x inches.

9. Find the heights at which normal-boned males and large-boned females would weigh the same.

8–2

Enrichment

Using Equations: Ideal Weight

You can find your ideal weight as follows.
A woman should weigh 100 pounds for the first 5 feet of height
and 5 additional pounds for each inch over 5 feet (5 feet =
60 inches). A man should weigh 106 pounds for the first 5 feet
of height and 6 additional pounds for each inch over 5 feet.
These formulas apply to people with normal bone structures.

To determine your bone structure, wrap your thumb and index
finger around the wrist of your other hand. If the thumb and
finger just touch, you have normal bone structure. If they
overlap, you are small-boned. If they don't overlap, you are
large-boned. Small-boned people should decrease their
calculated ideal weight by 10%. Large-boned people should
increase the value by 10%.

Calculate the ideal weights of these people.

1. woman, 5 ft 4 in., normal-boned
   120 lb

2. man, 5 ft 11 in., large-boned
   189.2 lb

3. man, 6 ft 5 in., small-boned
   187.2 lb

4. you, if you are at least 5 ft tall
   Answers will vary.

*Suppose a normal-boned man is x inches tall. If he is at
least 5 feet tall, then $x - 60$ represents the number of inches
this man is over 5 feet tall. For each of these inches, his
ideal weight is increased by 6 pounds. Thus, his proper
weight (y) is given by the formula $y = 6(x - 60) + 106$ or
$y = 6x - 254$. If the man is large-boned, the formula becomes
$y = 6x - 254 + 0.10(6x - 254)$.*

5. Write the formula for the weight of a large-boned man in
   slope-intercept form.
   $y = 6.6x - 279.4$

6. Derive the formula for the ideal weight (y) of a normal-
   boned female with height x inches. Write the formula in
   slope-intercept form.
   $y = 5x - 200$

7. Derive the formula in slope-intercept form for the ideal
   weight (y) of a large-boned female with height x inches.
   $y = 5.5x - 220$

8. Derive the formula in slope-intercept form for the ideal
   weight (y) of a small-boned male with height x inches.
   $y = 5.4x - 228.6$

9. Find the heights at which normal-boned males and large-
   boned females would weigh the same.
   68 in., or 5 ft 8 in.

Algebra 1

Arithmetic Series

An **arithmetic series** is a series in which each term after the first may be found by adding the same number to the preceding term. Let S stand for the following series in which each term is 3 more than the preceding one.

$S = 2 + 5 + 8 + 11 + 14 + 17 + 20$

The series remains the same if we reverse the order of all the terms. So let us reverse the order of the terms and add one series to the other, term by term. This is shown at the right.

$$S = 2 + 5 + 8 + 11 + 14 + 17 + 20$$
$$S = 20 + 17 + 14 + 11 + 8 + 5 + 2$$
$$2S = 22 + 22 + 22 + 22 + 22 + 22 + 22$$
$$2S = 7(22)$$
$$S = \frac{7(22)}{2} = 7(11) = 77$$

Let a represent the first term of the series.
Let l represent the last term of the series.
Let n represent the number of terms in the series.
In the preceding example, $a = 2$, $l = 20$, and $n = 7$. Notice that when you add the two series, term by term, the sum of each pair of terms is 22. That sum can be found by adding the first and last terms, $2 + 20$ or $a + l$. Notice also that there are 7, or n, such sums. Therefore, the value of $2S$ is $7(22)$, or $n(a + l)$ in the general case. Since this is twice the sum of the series, you can use the following formula to find the sum of any arithmetic series.

$$S = \frac{n(a + l)}{2}$$

Example 1: Find the sum: $1 + 2 + 3 + 4 + 5 + 6 + 7 + 8 + 9$

$a = 1$, $l = 9$, $n = 9$, so $S = \dfrac{9(1 + 9)}{2} = \dfrac{9 \cdot 10}{2} = 45$

Example 2: Find the sum: $-9 + (-5) + (-1) + 3 + 7 + 11 + 15$

$a = -9$, $l = 15$, $n = 7$, so $S = \dfrac{7(-9 + 15)}{2} = \dfrac{7 \cdot 6}{2} = 21$

Find the sum of each arithmetic series.

1. $3 + 6 + 9 + 12 + 15 + 18 + 21 + 24$

2. $10 + 15 + 20 + 25 + 30 + 35 + 40 + 45 + 50$

3. $-21 + (-16) + (-11) + (-6) + (-1) + 4 + 9 + 14$

4. even whole numbers from 2 through 100

5. odd whole numbers between 0 and 100

Arithmetic Series

An **arithmetic series** is a series in which each term after the first may be found by adding the same number to the preceding term. Let S stand for the following series in which each term is 3 more than the preceding one.

$S = 2 + 5 + 8 + 11 + 14 + 17 + 20$

The series remains the same if we reverse the order of all the terms. So let us reverse the order of the terms and add one series to the other, term by term. This is shown at the right.

$$\begin{aligned} S &= 2 + 5 + 8 + 11 + 14 + 17 + 20 \\ S &= 20 + 17 + 14 + 11 + 8 + 5 + 2 \\ \hline 2S &= 22 + 22 + 22 + 22 + 22 + 22 + 22 \\ 2S &= 7(22) \end{aligned}$$

$$S = \frac{7(22)}{2} = 7(11) = 77$$

Let a represent the first term of the series.
Let l represent the last term of the series.
Let n represent the number of terms in the series.
In the preceding example, $a = 2$, $l = 20$, and $n = 7$. Notice that when you add the two series, term by term, the sum of each pair of terms is 22. That sum can be found by adding the first and last terms, $2 + 20$ or $a + l$. Notice also that there are 7, or n, such sums. Therefore, the value of $2S$ is $7(22)$, or $n(a + l)$ in the general case. Since this is twice the sum of the series, you can use the following formula to find the sum of any arithmetic series.

$$S = \frac{n(a + l)}{2}$$

Example 1: Find the sum: $1 + 2 + 3 + 4 + 5 + 6 + 7 + 8 + 9$

$a = 1$, $l = 9$, $n = 9$, so $S = \dfrac{9(1 + 9)}{2} = \dfrac{9 \cdot 10}{2} = 45$

Example 2: Find the sum: $-9 + (-5) + (-1) + 3 + 7 + 11 + 15$

$a = -9$, $l = 15$, $n = 7$, so $S = \dfrac{7(-9 + 15)}{2} = \dfrac{7 \cdot 6}{2} = 21$

Find the sum of each arithmetic series.

1. $3 + 6 + 9 + 12 + 15 + 18 + 21 + 24$ **108**

2. $10 + 15 + 20 + 25 + 30 + 35 + 40 + 45 + 50$ **270**

3. $-21 + (-16) + (-11) + (-6) + (-1) + 4 + 9 + 14$ **−28**

4. even whole numbers from 2 through 100 **2550**

5. odd whole numbers between 0 and 100 **2500**

8-4

Enrichment

Geometric Vanishing Acts

Puzzles of this type use a "trick" drawing. It appears that rearranging the pieces of each figure causes one or more squares to disappear.

Make figures of your own on graph paper. Then explain the "trick" in each puzzle.

1. The rectangle has an area of 65 square units, but the square has an area of only 64 square units.

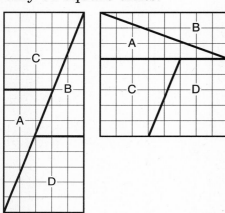

2. The square has an area of 64 square units, but the rectangle has an area of only 63 square units.

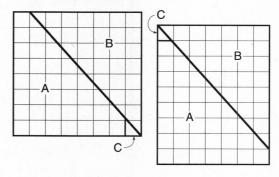

3. The square has an area of 64 units, but the new figure has an area of only 63 units.

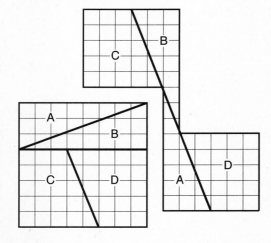

4. Rearranging the square on the left causes a 2-unit "hole" to appear.

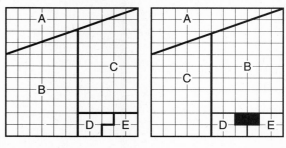

Enrichment

Geometric Vanishing Acts

Puzzles of this type use a "trick" drawing. It appears that rearranging the pieces of each figure causes one or more squares to disappear.

Make figures of your own on graph paper. Then explain the "trick" in each puzzle.

1. The rectangle has an area of 65 square units, but the square has an area of only 64 square units.

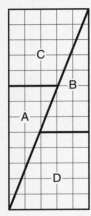 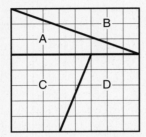

Pieces A and B are not triangles but quadrilaterals. In the second figure, they overlap.

2. The square has an area of 64 square units, but the rectangle has an area of only 63 square units.

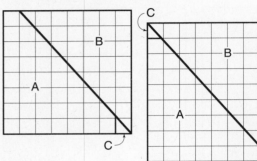

The triangle C actually has a height of $1\frac{1}{7}$ units, so the rectangle is really $9\frac{1}{7}$ units high.

3. The square has an area of 64 units, but the new figure has an area of only 63 units.

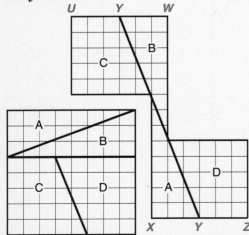

UVW and XYZ are not straight line segments. Thus, some "unit squares" of the second figure are not squares at all.

4. Rearranging the square on the left causes a 2-unit "hole" to appear.

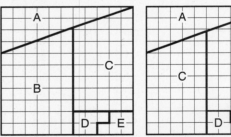

Piece A is a quadrilateral, not a triangle. Thus, in the second figure, the tops of pieces B and C overlap portions of piece A.

Describing Regions

The shaded region inside the triangle can be
described with a system of three inequalities.

$$y < -x + 1$$
$$y > \frac{1}{3}x - 3$$
$$y > -9x - 31$$

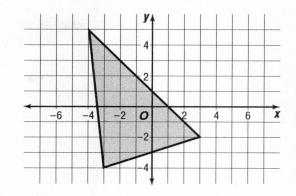

**Write systems of inequalities to describe each region. You may
first need to divide a region into triangles or quadrilaterals.**

1.

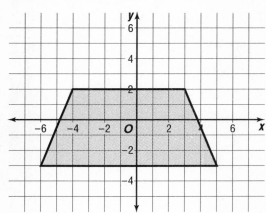

2.

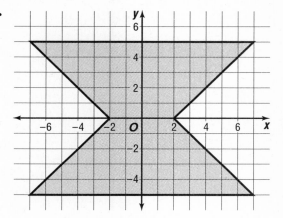

3.

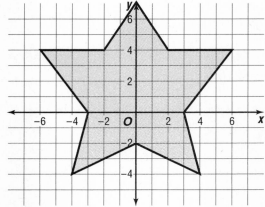

Enrichment

Describing Regions

The shaded region inside the triangle can be described with a system of three inequalities.

$$y < -x + 1$$
$$y > \frac{1}{3}x - 3$$
$$y > -9x - 31$$

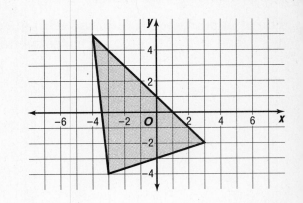

Write systems of inequalities to describe each region. You may first need to divide a region into triangles or quadrilaterals.

1.

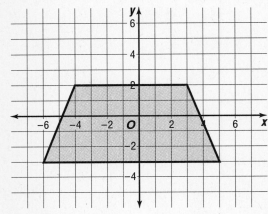

$y < \frac{5}{2}x + 12$

$y < -\frac{5}{2}x + 12$

$y < 2 \qquad y > -3$

2.

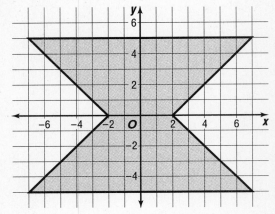

$y > -x - 2 \qquad y < x + 2$
$y > x - 2 \qquad y < -x + 2$
$y < 5 \qquad\quad y > -5$

3.

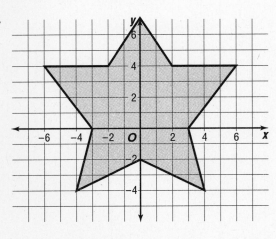

top: $y < \frac{3}{2}x + 7,\ y < -\frac{3}{2}x + 7,\ y > 4$

middle: $y < 4,\ y > 0,\ y > -\frac{4}{3}x - 4,$
$y > \frac{4}{3}x - 4$

bottom left: $y < 4x + 12,\ y > \frac{1}{2}x - 2,$
$y < 0,\ x < 0$

bottom right: $y < -4x + 12,$
$y > -\frac{1}{2}x - 2,\ y < 0,\ x < 0$

Algebra 1

Enrichment

Circular Areas and Volumes

Area of Circle	Volume of Cylinder	Volume of Cone
$A = \pi r^2$	$V = \pi r^2 h$	$V = \frac{1}{3}\pi r^2 h$

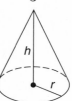

Write an algebraic expression for each shaded area. (Recall that the diameter of a circle is twice its radius.)

1.

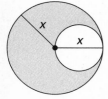

2.

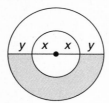

3.

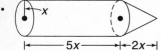

Write an algebraic expression of the total volume of each figure.

4.

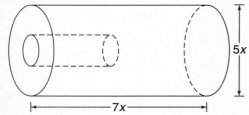

5.

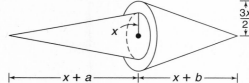

Each figure has a cylindrical hole with a radius of 2 inches and a height of 5 inches. Find each volume.

6.

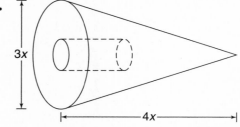

7.

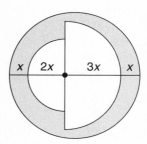

9-1

Enrichment

Circular Areas and Volumes

Area of Circle	Volume of Cylinder	Volume of Cone
$A = \pi r^2$	$V = \pi r^2 h$	$V = \frac{1}{3}\pi r^2 h$

 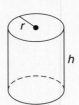 

Write an algebraic expression for each shaded area. (Recall that the diameter of a circle is twice its radius.)

1.

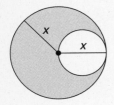

2.

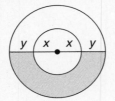

3.

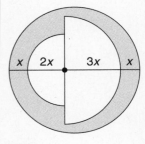

$$\pi x^2 - \pi\left(\frac{x}{2}\right)^2 = \frac{3}{4}\pi x^2 \qquad \frac{\pi}{2}(y^2 + 2xy) \qquad \frac{23\pi}{4}x^2$$

Write an algebraic expression of the total volume of each figure.

4.

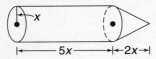

5.

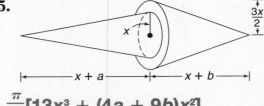

$$5\frac{2}{3}\pi x^3 \qquad\qquad \frac{\pi}{12}[13x^3 + (4a + 9b)x^2]$$

Each figure has a cylindrical hole with a radius of 2 inches and a height of 5 inches. Find each volume.

6.

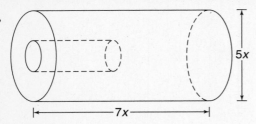

7.

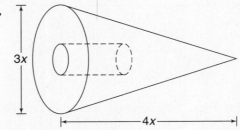

$$\frac{175\pi}{4}x^3 - 20\pi \text{ in}^3 \qquad\qquad 3\pi x^3 - 20\pi \text{ in}^3$$

NAME_____ DATE _____

Enrichment

Patterns with Powers

Use your calculator, if necessary, to complete each pattern.

a. $2^{10} =$ _____

$2^9 =$ _____

$2^8 =$ _____

$2^7 =$ _____

$2^6 =$ _____

$2^5 =$ _____

$2^4 =$ _____

$2^3 =$ _____

$2^2 =$ _____

$2^1 =$ _____

b. $5^{10} =$ _____

$5^9 =$ _____

$5^8 =$ _____

$5^7 =$ _____

$5^6 =$ _____

$5^5 =$ _____

$5^4 =$ _____

$5^3 =$ _____

$5^2 =$ _____

$5^1 =$ _____

c. $4^{10} =$ _____

$4^9 =$ _____

$4^8 =$ _____

$4^7 =$ _____

$4^6 =$ _____

$4^5 =$ _____

$4^4 =$ _____

$4^3 =$ _____

$4^2 =$ _____

$4^1 =$ _____

Study the patterns for a, b, and c above. Then answer the questions.

1. Describe the pattern of the exponents from the top of each column to the bottom.

2. Describe the pattern of the powers from the top of the column to the bottom.

3. What would you expect the following powers to be?

2^0 $\qquad\qquad$ 5^0 $\qquad\qquad$ 4^0

4. Write a rule. Test it on patterns that you obtain using -2, -5, and -4 as bases.

Study the pattern below. Then answer the questions.

$0^3 = 0$ $\quad$ $0^2 = 0$ $\quad$ $0^1 = 0$ $\quad$ $0^0 =$ ___?___ $\quad$ 0^{-1} does not exist.
0^{-2} does not exist. $\quad$ 0^{-3} does not exist.

5. Why do 0^{-1}, 0^{-2}, and 0^{-3} not exist?

6. Based upon the pattern, can you determine whether 0^0 exists?

7. The symbol 0^0 is called an **indeterminate,** which means that it has no unique value. Thus it does not exist as a unique real number. Why do you think that 0^0 cannot equal 1?

Algebra 1

Enrichment

Patterns with Powers

Use your calculator, if necessary, to complete each pattern.

a. 2^{10} = __1024__

2^9 = __512__

2^8 = __256__

2^7 = __128__

2^6 = __64__

2^5 = __32__

2^4 = __16__

2^3 = __8__

2^2 = __4__

2^1 = __2__

b. 5^{10} = __9,765,625__

5^9 = __1,953,125__

5^8 = __390,625__

5^7 = __78,125__

5^6 = __15,625__

5^5 = __3125__

5^4 = __625__

5^3 = __125__

5^2 = __25__

5^1 = __5__

c. 4^{10} = __1,048,576__

4^9 = __262,144__

4^8 = __65,536__

4^7 = __16,384__

4^6 = __4096__

4^5 = __1024__

4^4 = __256__

4^3 = __64__

4^2 = __16__

4^1 = __4__

Study the patterns for a, b, and c above. Then answer the questions.

1. Describe the pattern of the exponents from the top of each column to the bottom. **The exponents decrease by one from each row to the one below.**

2. Describe the pattern of the powers from the top of the column to the bottom. **To get each power, divide the power on the row above by the base (2, 5, or 4).**

3. What would you expect the following powers to be?

2^0 **1** 5^0 **1** 4^0 **1**

4. Write a rule. Test it on patterns that you obtain using -2, -5, and -4 as bases. **Any nonzero number to the zero power equals one.**

Study the pattern below. Then answer the questions.

$0^3 = 0$ $0^2 = 0$ $0^1 = 0$ $0^0 =$ __?__ 0^{-1} does not exist.
0^{-2} does not exist. 0^{-3} does not exist.

5. Why do 0^{-1}, 0^{-2}, and 0^{-3} not exist? **Negative exponents are not defined unless the base is nonzero.**

6. Based upon the pattern, can you determine whether 0^0 exists? **No, since the pattern $0^n = 0$ breaks down for $n < 1$.**

7. The symbol 0^0 is called an **indeterminate,** which means that it has no unique value. Thus it does not exist as a unique real number. Why do you think that 0^0 cannot equal 1? **Answers will vary. One answer is that if $0^0 = 1$, then $1 = \dfrac{1}{1} = \dfrac{1^0}{0^0} = \left(\dfrac{1}{0}\right)^0$, which is a false result, since division by zero is not allowed. Thus, 0^0 cannot equal 1.**

             Algebra 1

Enrichment

Converting Metric Units

Scientific notation is convenient to use for unit conversions in the metric system.

Example 1: How many kilometers are there in 4,300,000 meters?

Divide the measure by the number of meters (1000) in one kilometer. Express both numbers in scientific notation.

$$\frac{4.3 \times 10^6}{1 \times 10^3} = 4.3 \times 10^3 \qquad \text{The answer is } 4.3 \times 10^3 \text{ km.}$$

Example 2: Convert 3700 grams into milligrams.

Multiply by the number of milligrams (1000) in 1 gram.

$$(3.7 \times 10^3)(1 \times 10^3) = 3.7 \times 10^6 \qquad \text{There are } 3.7 \times 10^6 \text{ mg in 3700 g.}$$

Complete the following. Express each answer in scientific notation.

1. 250,000 m = _____ km

2. 375 km = _____ m

3. 247 m = _____ cm

4. 5000 m = _____ mm

5. 0.0004 km = _____ m

6. 0.01 mm = _____ m

7. 6000 m = _____ mm

8. 340 cm = _____ km

9. 52,000 mg = _____ g

10. 420 kL = _____ L

Solve.

11. The planet Mars has a diameter of 6.76×10^3 km. What is the diameter of Mars in meters? Express the answer in both scientific and decimal notation.

12. The distance of the earth from the sun is 149,590,000 km. Light travels 3.0×10^8 meters per second. How long does it take light from the sun to reach the earth in minutes?

13. A light-year is the distance that light travels in one year. (See Exercise 12.) How far is a light year in kilometers? Express your answer in scientific notation.

Enrichment

Converting Metric Units

Scientific notation is convenient to use for unit conversions in the metric system.

Example 1: How many kilometers are there in 4,300,000 meters?

Divide the measure by the number of meters (1000) in one kilometer. Express both numbers in scientific notation.

$$\frac{4.3 \times 10^6}{1 \times 10^3} = 4.3 \times 10^3 \qquad \text{The answer is } 4.3 \times 10^3 \text{ km.}$$

Example 2: Convert 3700 grams into milligrams.

Multiply by the number of milligrams (1000) in 1 gram.

$$(3.7 \times 10^3)(1 \times 10^3) = 3.7 \times 10^6 \qquad \text{There are } 3.7 \times 10^6 \text{ mg in 3700 g.}$$

Complete the following. Express each answer in scientific notation.

1. 250,000 m = _2.5×10^2_ km

2. 375 km = _3.75×10^5_ m

3. 247 m = _2.47×10^4_ cm

4. 5000 m = _5.0×10^6_ mm

5. 0.0004 km = _4.0×10^{-1}_ m

6. 0.01 mm = _1.0×10^{-5}_ m

7. 6000 m = _6×10^{-6}_ mm

8. 340 cm = _3.4×10^{-3}_ km

9. 52,000 mg = _5.2×10^1_ g

10. 420 kL = _4.2×10^5_ L

Solve.

11. The planet Mars has a diameter of 6.76×10^3 km. What is the diameter of Mars in meters? Express the answer in both scientific and decimal notation.
6,760,000 m; 6.76×10^6 m

12. The distance of the earth from the sun is 149,590,000 km. Light travels 3.0×10^8 meters per second. How long does it take light from the sun to reach the earth in minutes?
8.31 min

13. A light-year is the distance that light travels in one year. (See Exercise 12.) How far is a light year in kilometers? Express your answer in scientific notation.
9.46×10^{12} km

NAME_____ DATE _____

Enrichment

Rep-Tiles

A rep-tile is a figure that can be subdivided into smaller copies of itself. The large figure is similar to the small ones and the small figures are all congruent.

Show that each figure is a rep-tile by subdividing it into four smaller and similar figures.

1.

2.

3.

4.

5.

6.

Subdivide each rep-tile into nine smaller and similar figures.

7.

8.

9.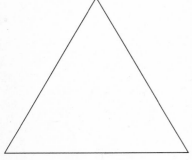

10.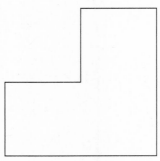

Algebra 1

NAME_____ DATE _____

Enrichment

Student Edition
Pages 514–519

Rep-Tiles

A rep-tile is a figure that can be subdivided into smaller copies of itself. The large figure is similar to the small ones and the small figures are all congruent.

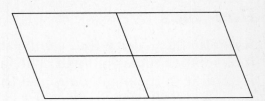

Show that each figure is a rep-tile by subdividing it into four smaller and similar figures.

1.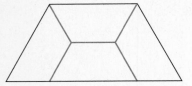

2.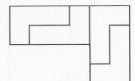

3.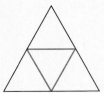

4.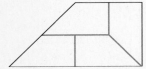

5.

6.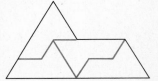

Subdivide each rep-tile into nine smaller and similar figures.

7.

8.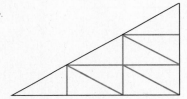

9.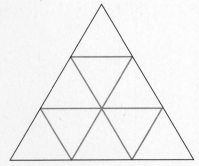

10.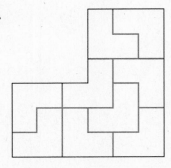

Algebra 1

9–5

Enrichment

Counting-Off Puzzles

Solve each puzzle.

1. Twenty-five people are standing in a circle. Starting with person 1, they count off from 1 to 7 and then start over with 1. Each person who says "7" drops out of the circle. Who is the last person left?

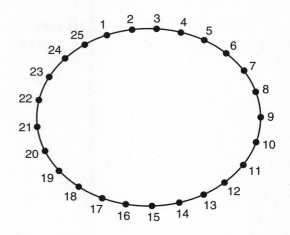

2. Forty people stand in a circle. They count off so that every third person drops out. Which two people are the last ones left?

3. Only half of the 30 students in Sharon's class can go on a field trip. Sharon arranges the boys and girls as shown. They count off from 1 to 9 and every ninth person drops out until only 15 people are left. Who gets to go on the field trip.

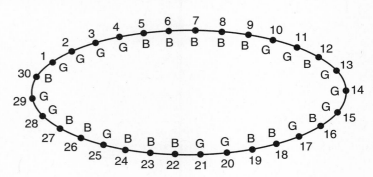

A group of people stand in a circle and count off 1, 2, 1, 2, 1 and so on. Every second person drops out. Person number 1 is the last person left.

4. Draw a diagram to show why the number of people in the circle must be even. Then, explain your answer.

5. When the count returns to person number 1 for the first time, how many people have dropped out?

6. Find the number of people in the circle if the number is between 10 and 20. Do the same if the number is between 30 and 40. What can you conclude about the original number of people?

Algebra 1

Enrichment

Counting-Off Puzzles

Solve each puzzle.

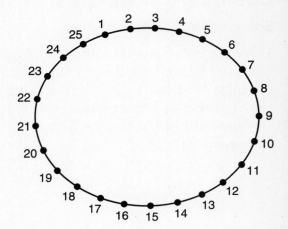

1. Twenty-five people are standing in a circle. Starting with person 1, they count off from 1 to 7 and then start over with 1. Each person who says "7" drops out of the circle. Who is the last person left?
number 15

2. Forty people stand in a circle. They count off so that every third person drops out. Which two people are the last ones left?
13th and 28th people

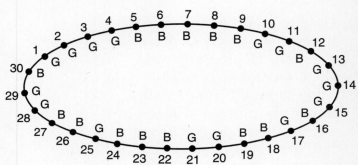

3. Only half of the 30 students in Sharon's class can go on a field trip. Sharon arranges the boys and girls as shown. They count off from 1 to 9 and every ninth person drops out until only 15 people are left. Who gets to go on the field trip. **the girls**

A group of people stand in a circle and count off 1, 2, 1, 2, 1 and so on. Every second person drops out. Person number 1 is the last person left.

4. Draw a diagram to show why the number of people in the circle must be even. Then, explain your answer. **If the number is odd, person 1 would drop out after the first round.**

5. When the count returns to person number 1 for the first time, how many people have dropped out? **half of the original number**

6. Find the number of people in the circle if the number is between 10 and 20. Do the same if the number is between 30 and 40. What can you conclude about the original number of people? **16; 32; The number must be a power of 2.**

Enrichment

Geometric Series

The terms of this polynomial form a geometric series.

$$a + ar + ar^2 + ar^3 + ar^4$$

The first term is the constant a. Then each term after that is found by multiplying by a constant multiplier r.

Use the equation $S = a + ar + ar^2 + ar^3 + ar^4$ for Exercises 1–3.

1. Multiply each side of the equation by r.

2. Subtract the original equation from your result in Exercise 1.

3. Solve the result from Exercise 2 for the variable S.

Use the polynomial $a + ar + ar^2 + ar^3 + ar^4 + \cdots + ar^{n-1}$ for Exercises 4–8.

4. Write the 10th term of the polynomial.

5. If $a = 5$ and $r = 2$, what is the 8th term?

6. Follow the steps in Exercises 1–3 to write a formula for the sum of this polynomial.

7. If the 3rd term is 20 and the 6th term is 160, solve for r^3 and then find r. Then solve $ar^2 = 20$ for a and find the value of the first six terms of the polynomial.

8. Find the sum of the first six terms of the geometric series that begins 3, 6, 12, 24, ⋯. First write the values for a and r.

NAME_____ DATE _____

Enrichment

Geometric Series

The terms of this polynomial form a geometric series.

$$a + ar + ar^2 + ar^3 + ar^4$$

The first term is the constant a. Then each term after that is found by multiplying by a constant multiplier r.

Use the equation $S = a + ar + ar^2 + ar^3 + ar^4$ for Exercises 1–3.

1. Multiply each side of the equation by r.
   $rS = ar + ar^2 + ar^3 + ar^4 + ar^5$

2. Subtract the original equation from your result in Exercise 1.
   $rS - S = ar^5 - a$

3. Solve the result from Exercise 2 for the variable S. $S = \dfrac{a(r^5 - 1)}{r - 1}$

Use the polynomial $a + ar + ar^2 + ar^3 + ar^4 + \cdots + ar^{n-1}$ for Exercises 4–8.

4. Write the 10th term of the polynomial. ar^9

5. If $a = 5$ and $r = 2$, what is the 8th term? $ar^7 = 640$

6. Follow the steps in Exercises 1–3 to write a formula for the sum of this polynomial. $S = \dfrac{a(r^n - 1)}{r - 1}$

7. If the 3rd term is 20 and the 6th term is 160, solve for r^3 and then find r. Then solve $ar^2 = 20$ for a and find the value of the first six terms of the polynomial.
   $\dfrac{ar^5}{ar^2} = \dfrac{160}{20}$, $r^3 = 8$, $r = 2$; $ar^2 = 20$; $a = 5$; 5, 10, 20, 40, 80, 160

8. Find the sum of the first six terms of the geometric series that begins 3, 6, 12, 24, $\cdots$. First write the values for a and r.
   $a = 3$, $r = 2$
   $S = \dfrac{3(2^6 - 1)}{2 - 1} = 3 \times 63 = 189$

9-7

Enrichment

Powers of Binomials

This arrangement of numbers is called Pascal's Triangle. It was first published in 1665, but was known hundreds of years earlier.

$$
\begin{array}{ccccccccc}
 & & & & 1 & & & & \\
 & & & 1 & & 1 & & & \\
 & & 1 & & 2 & & 1 & & \\
 & 1 & & 3 & & 3 & & 1 & \\
1 & & 4 & & 6 & & 4 & & 1
\end{array}
$$

1. Each number in the triangle is found by adding two numbers. What two numbers were added to get the 6 in the 5th row?

2. Describe how to create the 6th row of Pascal's Triangle.

3. Write the numbers for rows 6 through 10 of the triangle.

Row 6:

Row 7:

Row 8:

Row 9:

Row 10:

Multiply to find the expanded form of each product.

4. $(a + b)^2$

5. $(a + b)^3$

6. $(a + b)^4$

Now compare the coefficients of the three products in Exercises 4–6 with Pascal's Triangle.

7. Describe the relationship between the expanded form of $(a + b)^n$ and Pascal's Triangle.

8. Use Pascal's Triangle to write the expanded form of $(a + b)^6$.

Enrichment

Powers of Binomials

This arrangement of numbers is called Pascal's Triangle. It was first published in 1665, but was known hundreds of years earlier.

```
          1
        1   1
      1   2   1
    1   3   3   1
  1   4   6   4   1
```

1. Each number in the triangle is found by adding two numbers. What two numbers were added to get the 6 in the 5th row?
   3 and 3

2. Describe how to create the 6th row of Pascal's Triangle.
   The first and last numbers are 1. Evaluate 1 + 4, 4 + 6, 6 + 4, and 4 + 1 to find the other numbers.

3. Write the numbers for rows 6 through 10 of the triangle.

   Row 6: **1   5   10   10   5   1**

   Row 7: **1   6   15   20   15   6   1**

   Row 8: **1   7   21   35   35   21   7   1**

   Row 9: **1   8   28   56   70   56   28   8   1**

   Row 10: **1   9   37   84   126   126   84   37   9   1**

Multiply to find the expanded form of each product.

4. $(a + b)^2$ $a^2 + 2ab + b^2$

5. $(a + b)^3$ $a^3 + 3a^2b + 3ab^2 + b^3$

6. $(a + b)^4$ $a^4 + 4a^3b + 6a^2b^2 + 4ab^3 + b^4$

Now compare the coefficients of the three products in Exercises 4–6 with Pascal's Triangle.

7. Describe the relationship between the expanded form of $(a + b)^n$ and Pascal's Triangle. **The coefficients of the expanded form are found in row $n + 1$ of Pascal's Triangle.**

8. Use Pascal's Triangle to write the expanded form of $(a + b)^6$.
   $a^6 + 6a^5b + 15a^4b^2 + 20a^3b^3 + 15a^2b^4 + 6ab^5 + b^6$

Algebra 1

Enrichment

Special Polynomial Products

Sometimes the product of two polynomials can be found readily with the use of one of the special products of binomials.

For example, you can find the square of a trinomial by recalling the square of a binomial.

Example 1: Find $(x + y + z)^2$.

$$(a + b)^2 = a^2 + 2 \cdot a \cdot b + b^2$$

$$[(x + y) + z]^2 = (x + y)^2 + 2(x + y)z + z^2$$

$$= x^2 + 2xy + y^2 + 2xz + 2yz + z^2$$

Example 2: Find $(3t + x + 1)(3t - x - 1)$.

(*Hint:* $(3t + x + 1)(3t - x - 1)$ is the product of a sum $3t + (x + 1)$ and a difference $3t - (x + 1)$.)

$$(3t + x + 1)(3t - x - 1) = [3t + (x + 1)][3t - (x + 1)]$$

$$= 9t^2 - (x + 1)^2$$

$$= 9t^2 - x^2 - 2x - 1$$

Use a special product of binomials to find each product.

1. $(x + y - z)^2$

2. $(r + s + 5)^2$

3. $(b - 3 + d)^2$

4. $(k - m - 2)^2$

5. $(x + 1 + 2b)(x + 1 - 2b)$

6. $(y - 2 + x)(y - 2 - x)$

7. $(5 + b - x)(5 + b + x)$

8. $(j - 5 - f)(j + 5 + f)$

9. $[(x + y) + (z + w)][(x + y) - (z + w)]$

10. $(2a + 1 + 3b - c)(2a + 1 - 3b + c)$

NAME_____ DATE _____

Enrichment

Special Polynomial Products

Sometimes the product of two polynomials can be found readily with the use of one of the special products of binomials.

For example, you can find the square of a trinomial by recalling the square of a binomial.

Example 1: Find $(x + y + z)^2$.

$$(a + b)^2 = a^2 + 2 \cdot a \cdot b + b^2$$

$$[(x + y) + z]^2 = (x + y)^2 + 2(x + y)z + z^2$$

$$= x^2 + 2xy + y^2 + 2xz + 2yz + z^2$$

Example 2: Find $(3t + x + 1)(3t - x - 1)$.

(*Hint:* $(3t + x + 1)(3t - x - 1)$ is the product of a sum $3t + (x + 1)$ and a difference $3t - (x + 1)$.)

$$(3t + x + 1)(3t - x - 1) = [3t + (x + 1)][3t - (x + 1)]$$

$$= 9t^2 - (x + 1)^2$$

$$= 9t^2 - x^2 - 2x - 1$$

Use a special product of binomials to find each product.

1. $(x + y - z)^2$
$x^2 + 2xy - 2xz + y^2 - 2yz + z^2$

2. $(r + s + 5)^2$
$r^2 + 2rs + s^2 + 10r + 10s + 25$

3. $(b - 3 + d)^2$
$b^2 - 6b + 2bd + 9 - 6d + d^2$

4. $(k - m - 2)^2$
$k^2 - 2km + m^2 - 4k + 4m + 4$

5. $(x + 1 + 2b)(x + 1 - 2b)$
$x^2 + 2x + 1 - 4b^2$

6. $(y - 2 + x)(y - 2 - x)$
$y^2 - 4y + 4 - x^2$

7. $(5 + b - x)(5 + b + x)$
$25 + 10b + b^2 - x^2$

8. $(j - 5 - f)(j + 5 + f)$
$j^2 - f^2 - 10f - 25$

9. $[(x + y) + (z + w)][(x + y) - (z + w)]$
$x^2 + 2xy + y^2 - z^2 - 2zw - w^2$

10. $(2a + 1 + 3b - c)(2a + 1 - 3b + c)$
$4a^2 + 4a + 1 - 9b^2 + 6bc - c^2$

10-1

Enrichment

Finding the GCF by Euclid's Algorithm

Finding the greatest common factor of two large numbers can take a long time using prime factorizations. This method can be avoided by using *Euclid's Algorithm* as shown in the following example.

Example: Find the GCF of 209 and 532.

Divide the greater number, 532, by the lesser, 209.

$$
\begin{array}{r}
2 \\
209{\overline{)532}} \\
418 \\
\end{array}
$$

Divide the remainder
into the divisor above.
Repeat this process
until the remainder
is zero. The last
nonzero remainder is
the GCF.

$$
\begin{array}{r}
1 \\
114{\overline{)209}} \\
114 \\
\end{array}
\quad
\begin{array}{r}
1 \\
95{\overline{)114}} \\
95 \\
\end{array}
\quad
\begin{array}{r}
5 \\
19{\overline{)95}} \\
95 \\
\hline
0
\end{array}
$$

The divisor, 19, is the GCF of 209 and 532.

Suppose the GCF of two numbers is found to be 1. Then the numbers are said to be **relatively prime**.

Find the GCF of each group of numbers by using Euclid's Algorithm.

1. 187; 578

2. 1802; 106

3. 161; 943

4. 215; 1849

5. 1325; 3498

6. 3484; 5963

7. 33,583; 4257

8. 453; 484

9. 95; 209; 589

10. 518; 407; 851

11. $17a^2x^2z$; $1615axz^2$

12. $752cf^3$; $893c^3f^3$

13. $979r^2s^2$; $495rs^3$, $154r^3s^3$

14. $360x^5y^7$; $328xy$; $568x^3y^3$

Finding the GCF by Euclid's Algorithm

Finding the greatest common factor of two large numbers can take a long time using prime factorizations. This method can be avoided by using *Euclid's Algorithm* as shown in the following example.

Example: Find the GCF of 209 and 532.

Divide the greater number, 532, by the lesser, 209.

$$\begin{array}{r} 2 \\ 209\overline{)532} \\ \underline{418} \end{array}$$

Divide the remainder
into the divisor above.
Repeat this process
until the remainder
is zero. The last
nonzero remainder is
the GCF.

$$\begin{array}{r} 1 \\ 114\overline{)209} \\ \underline{114} \end{array}$$

$$\begin{array}{r} 1 \\ 95\overline{)114} \\ \underline{95} \end{array}$$

$$\begin{array}{r} 5 \\ 19\overline{)95} \\ \underline{95} \\ 0 \end{array}$$

The divisor, 19, is the GCF of 209 and 532.

Suppose the GCF of two numbers is found to be 1. Then the numbers are said to be **relatively prime.**

Find the GCF of each group of numbers by using Euclid's Algorithm.

1. 187; 578 **17**

2. 1802; 106 **106**

3. 161; 943 **23**

4. 215; 1849 **43**

5. 1325; 3498 **53**

6. 3484; 5963 **67**

7. 33,583; 4257 **473**

8. 453; 484 **1**

9. 95; 209; 589 **19**

10. 518; 407; 851 **37**

11. $17a^2x^2z$; $1615axz^2$ **17axz**

12. $752cf^3$; $893c^3f^3$ **47cf³**

13. $979r^2s^2$; $495rs^3$, $154r^3s^3$ **11rs²**

14. $360x^5y^7$; $328xy$; $568x^3y^3$ **8xy**

Algebra 1

Enrichment

Factoring Trinomials of Fourth Degree

Some trinomials of the form $a^4 + a^2b^2 + b^4$ can be written as the difference of two squares and then factored.

Example: Factor $4x^4 - 37x^2y^2 + 9y^4$.

Step 1: Find the square roots of the first and last terms.

$$\sqrt{4x^4} = 2x^2 \qquad \sqrt{9y^4} = 3y^2$$

Step 2: Find twice the product of the square roots.

$$2(2x^2)(3y^2) = 12x^2y^2$$

Step 3: Separate the middle term into two parts. One part is either your answer to Step 2 or its opposite. The other part should be the opposite of a perfect square.

$$-37x^2y^2 = -12x^2y^2 - 25x^2y^2$$

Step 4: Rewrite the trinomial as the difference of two squares and then factor.

$$
\begin{aligned}
4x^4 - 37x^2y^2 + 9y^4 &= (4x^4 - 12x^2y^2 + 9y^4) - 25x^2y^2 \\
&= (2x^2 - 3y^2)^2 - 25x^2y^2 \\
&= [(2x^2 - 3y^2) + 5xy][(2x^2 - 3y^2) - 5xy] \\
&= (2x^2 + 5xy - 3y^2)(2x^2 - 5xy - 3y^2)
\end{aligned}
$$

Factor each trinomial.

1. $x^4 + x^2y^2 + y^4$

2. $x^4 + x^2 + 1$

3. $9a^4 - 15a^2 + 1$

4. $16a^4 - 17a^2 + 1$

5. $4a^4 - 13a^2 + 1$

6. $9a^4 + 26a^2b^2 + 25b^4$

7. $4x^4 - 21x^2y^2 + 9y^4$

8. $4a^4 - 29a^2c^2 + 25c^4$

Enrichment

Factoring Trinomials of Fourth Degree

Some trinomials of the form $a^4 + a^2b^2 + b^4$ can be written as the difference of two squares and then factored.

Example: Factor $4x^4 - 37x^2y^2 + 9y^4$.

Step 1: Find the square roots of the first and last terms.

$$\sqrt{4x^4} = 2x^2 \qquad \sqrt{9y^4} = 3y^2$$

Step 2: Find twice the product of the square roots.

$$2(2x^2)(3y^2) = 12x^2y^2$$

Step 3: Separate the middle term into two parts. One part is either your answer to Step 2 or its opposite. The other part should be the opposite of a perfect square.

$$-37x^2y^2 = -12x^2y^2 - 25x^2y^2$$

Step 4: Rewrite the trinomial as the difference of two squares and then factor.

$$\begin{aligned} 4x^4 - 37x^2y^2 + 9y^4 &= (4x^4 - 12x^2y^2 + 9y^4) - 25x^2y^2 \\ &= (2x^2 - 3y^2)^2 - 25x^2y^2 \\ &= [(2x^2 - 3y^2) + 5xy][(2x^2 - 3y^2) - 5xy] \\ &= (2x^2 + 5xy - 3y^2)(2x^2 - 5xy - 3y^2) \end{aligned}$$

Factor each trinomial.

1. $x^4 + x^2y^2 + y^4$
   $(x^2 + xy + y^2)(x^2 - xy + y^2)$

2. $x^4 + x^2 + 1$
   $(x^2 + x + 1)(x^2 - x + 1)$

3. $9a^4 - 15a^2 + 1$
   $(3a^2 + 3a - 1)(3a^2 - 3a - 1)$

4. $16a^4 - 17a^2 + 1$
   $(4a - 1)(a + 1)(4a + 1)(a - 1)$

5. $4a^4 - 13a^2 + 1$
   $(2a^2 + 3a - 1)(2a^2 - 3a - 1)$

6. $9a^4 + 26a^2b^2 + 25b^4$
   $(3a^2 + 2ab + 5b^2)(3a^2 - 2ab + 5b^2)$

7. $4x^4 - 21x^2y^2 + 9y^4$
   $(2x^2 + 3xy - 3y^2)(2x^2 - 3xy - 3y^2)$

8. $4a^4 - 29a^2c^2 + 25c^4$
   $(2a + 5c)(a - c)(2a - 5c)(a + c)$

Area Models for Quadratic Trinomials

After you have factored a quadratic trinomial, you can use the factors to draw geometric models of the trinomial.

$x^2 + 5x - 6 = (x - 1)(x + 6)$

To draw a rectangular model, the value 2 was used for x so that the shorter side would have a length of 1. Then the drawing was done in centimeters. So, the area of the rectangle is $x^2 + 5x - 6$.

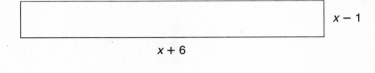

$x - 1$

$x + 6$

To draw a right triangle model, recall that the area of a triangle is one-half the base times the height. So, one of the sides must be twice as long as the shorter side of the rectangular model.

$2x - 2$

$x + 6$

$x^2 + 5x - 6 = (x - 1)(x + 6)$
$\qquad\qquad\quad = \frac{1}{2}(2x - 2)(x + 6)$

The area of the right triangle is also $x^2 + 5x - 6$.

Factor each trinomial. Then follow the directions to draw each model of the trinomial.

1. $x^2 + 2x - 3$ Use $x = 2$. Draw a rectangle in centimeters.

2. $3x^2 + 5x - 2$ Use $x = 1$. Draw a rectangle in centimeters.

3. $x^2 - 4x + 3$ Use $x = 4$. Draw two different right triangles in centimeters.

4. $9x^2 - 9x + 2$ Use $x = 2$. Draw two different right triangles. Use 0.5 centimeter for each unit.

10-3

Enrichment

Area Models for Quadratic Trinomials

After you have factored a quadratic trinomial, you can use the factors to draw geometric models of the trinomial.

$x^2 + 5x - 6 = (x - 1)(x + 6)$

To draw a rectangular model, the value 2 was used for x so that the shorter side would have a length of 1. Then the drawing was done in centimeters. So, the area of the rectangle is $x^2 + 5x - 6$.

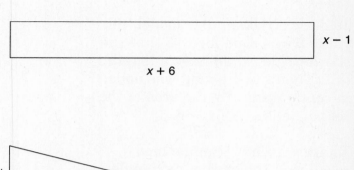

To draw a right triangle model, recall that the area of a triangle is one-half the base times the height. So, one of the sides must be twice as long as the shorter side of the rectangular model.

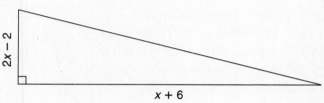

$x^2 + 5x - 6 = (x - 1)(x + 6)$
$\qquad = \frac{1}{2}(2x - 2)(x + 6)$

The area of the right triangle is also $x^2 + 5x - 6$.

Factor each trinomial. Then follow the directions to draw each model of the trinomial.

1. $x^2 + 2x - 3$ \qquad Use $x = 2$. Draw a rectangle in centimeters.
(x + 3)(x − 1)

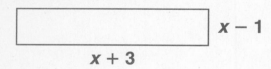

2. $3x^2 + 5x - 2$ \qquad Use $x = 1$. Draw a rectangle in centimeters.
(x + 2)(3x − 1)

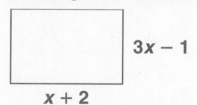

3. $x^2 - 4x + 3$ \qquad Use $x = 4$. Draw two different right triangles in centimeters. **(x − 1)(x − 3)**

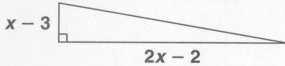

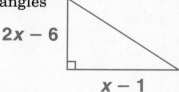

4. $9x^2 - 9x + 2$ \qquad Use $x = 2$. Draw two different right triangles. Use 0.5 centimeter for each unit. **(3x − 2)(3x − 1)**

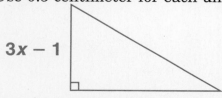

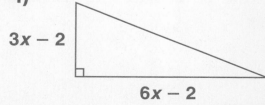

NAME_____ DATE _____

Enrichment

Writing Expressions of Area in Factored Form

Write an expression in factored form for the area A of the shaded region in each figure below.

1.

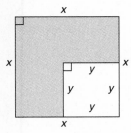

2.

3.

4.

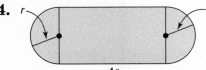

5.

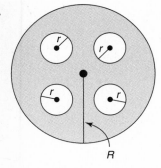

6.

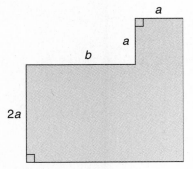

7.

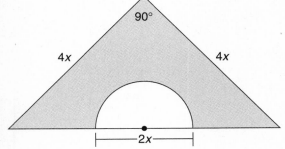

8.

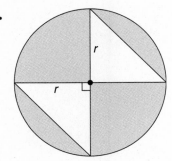

Algebra 1

Writing Expressions of Area in Factored Form

Write an expression in factored form for the area A of the shaded region in each figure below.

1.

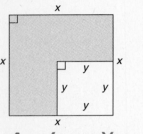

$$A = (x + y)(x - y)$$

2.

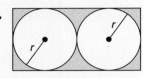

$$A = 2r^2(4 - \pi)$$

3.

$$A = \frac{\pi}{8}(a + b)(a - b)$$

4.

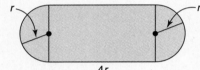

$$A = r^2(8 + \pi)$$

5.

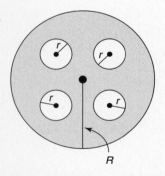

$$A = \pi(R + 2r)(R - 2r)$$

6.

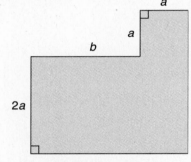

$$A = a(3a + 2b)$$

7.

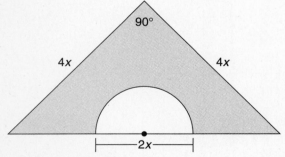

$$A = x^2\left(8 - \frac{\pi}{2}\right)$$

8.

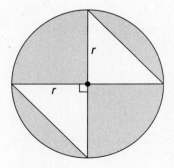

$$A = r^2(\pi - 1)$$

Algebra 1

10-5

Enrichment

Squaring Numbers: A Shortcut

A shortcut helps you to square a positive two-digit number ending in 5. The method is developed using the idea that a two-digit number may be expressed as $10t + u$. Suppose $u = 5$.

$$(10t + 5)^2 = (10t + 5)(10t + 5)$$
$$= 100t^2 + 50t + 50t + 25$$
$$= 100t^2 + 100t + 25$$
$$(10t + 5)^2 = 100t(t + 1) + 25$$

In words, this formula says that the square of a two-digit number has $t(t + 1)$ in the hundreds place. Then 2 is the tens digit and 5 is the units digit.

Example: Using the formula for $(10t + 5)^2$, find 85^2.
$$85^2 = 100 \cdot 8 \cdot (8 + 1) + 25$$
$$= 7200 + 25$$
$$= 7225 \qquad \textit{Shortcut: First think } 8 \cdot 9 = 72.$$
$$\textit{Then write 25.}$$

Thus, to square a number, such as 85, you can write the product of the tens digit and the next consecutive integer $t + 1$. Then write 25.

Find each of the following using the shortcut.

1. 15^2

2. 25^2

3. 35^2

4. 45^2

5. 55^2

6. 65^2

Solve each problem.

7. What is the tens digit in the square of 95?

8. What are the first two digits in the square of 75?

9. Any three-digit number can be written as $100a + 10b + c$. Square this expression to show that if the last digit of a three-digit number is 5 then the last two digits of the square of the number are 2 and 5.

10-5

Enrichment

Squaring Numbers: A Shortcut

A shortcut helps you to square a positive two-digit number ending in 5. The method is developed using the idea that a two-digit number may be expressed as $10t + u$. Suppose $u = 5$.

$$(10t + 5)^2 = (10t + 5)(10t + 5)$$
$$= 100t^2 + 50t + 50t + 25$$
$$= 100t^2 + 100t + 25$$
$$(10t + 5)^2 = 100t(t + 1) + 25$$

In words, this formula says that the square of a two-digit number has $t(t + 1)$ in the hundreds place. Then 2 is the tens digit and 5 is the units digit.

Example: Using the formula for $(10t + 5)^2$, find 85^2.
$$85^2 = 100 \cdot 8 \cdot (8 + 1) + 25$$
$$= 7200 + 25$$
$$= 7225 \qquad \textit{Shortcut: First think } 8 \cdot 9 = 72.$$
$$\textit{Then write 25.}$$

Thus, to square a number, such as 85, you can write the product of the tens digit and the next consecutive integer $t + 1$. Then write 25.

Find each of the following using the shortcut.

1. 15^2 **225**

2. 25^2 **625**

3. 35^2 **1225**

4. 45^2 **2025**

5. 55^2 **3025**

6. 65^2 **4225**

Solve each problem.

7. What is the tens digit in the square of 95? **2**

8. What are the first two digits in the square of 75? **56**

9. Any three-digit number can be written as $100a + 10b + c$. Square this expression to show that if the last digit of a three-digit number is 5 then the last two digits of the square of the number are 2 and 5.
$10{,}000a^2 + 2000ab + 200ac + 100b^2 + 20bc + c^2 =$
$10{,}000a^2 + 2000ab + 1000a + 100b^2 + 100b + 25$
The last two digits are not affected by the first five terms.

Using Factoring

The right side of each formula is a fraction. Factor the numerator and denominator of each fraction. Then reduce the fraction to simplest terms if possible. Use the result to answer the questions about each formula.

1. $t = \dfrac{\pi(d + r)^2 w - \pi r^2 w}{hws}$

where t = the approximate number of minutes of playing time remaining on a tape

d = the depth of the tape in inches

r = the radius of the core in inches

w = the width of the tape in inches

h = the thickness of the tape in inches

and s = the speed at which the tape is played in inches per minute

Find the approximate number of minutes left on a tape where

$d = \dfrac{5}{8}$, $r = \dfrac{7}{16}$, $w = \dfrac{3}{32}$, $h = 0.0015$, $s = 100$, and $\pi = 3.14$.

2. $R = \dfrac{M^2 v^2 + 2eM^2 v^2 + e^2 M^2 v^2}{2gM^2 + 4gMm + 2gm^2}$

where m = the mass of a golf ball in grams

M = the mass of a golf-club head in grams

v = the velocity of the club head in meters per second

e = the coefficient of restitution between the ball and the club head

g = the acceleration due to gravity (9.8 meters per second per second)

and R = the maximum range of the golf ball in meters

The value e, coefficient of restitution, is a measure of how elastic a golf ball is. As the temperature increases, the ball becomes more elastic. At 32°F, the value of e is about 0.64. At 80°F, the value of e is about 0.75. The mass of a golf ball is about 50 grams. Assume the mass of the club head is 250 grams and the velocity of the club head is 45 meters/second.

a. Find the maximum range at 32°F in meters and convert it to yards (1 m = 1.093 yds). Round your answers to the nearest whole number.

b. Find the maximum range at 80°F in meters and yards to the nearest whole number.

c. Why might a golfer want to buy a battery-heated glove to keep spare golf balls warm?

Enrichment

Using Factoring

The right side of each formula is a fraction. Factor the numerator and denominator of each fraction. Then reduce the fraction to simplest terms if possible. Use the result to answer the questions about each formula.

1. $t = \dfrac{\pi(d + r)^2 w - \pi r^2 w}{hws}$ where t = the approximate number of minutes of playing time remaining on a tape
d = the depth of the tape in inches
r = the radius of the core in inches
w = the width of the tape in inches
h = the thickness of the tape in inches
and s = the speed at which the tape is played in inches per minute

Find the approximate number of minutes left on a tape where

$d = \dfrac{5}{8}$, $r = \dfrac{7}{16}$, $w = \dfrac{3}{32}$, $h = 0.0015$, $s = 100$, and $\pi = 3.14$.

19.6 minutes

2. $R = \dfrac{M^2 v^2 + 2eM^2 v^2 + e^2 M^2 v^2}{2gM^2 + 4gMm + 2gm^2}$ where m = the mass of a golf ball in grams
M = the mass of a golf-club head in grams
v = the velocity of the club head in meters per second
e = the coefficient of restitution between the ball and the club head
g = the acceleration due to gravity (9.8 meters per second per second)
and R = the maximum range of the golf ball in meters

The value e, coefficient of restitution, is a measure of how elastic a golf ball is. As the temperature increases, the ball becomes more elastic. At 32°F, the value of e is about 0.64. At 80°F, the value of e is about 0.75. The mass of a golf ball is about 50 grams. Assume the mass of the club head is 250 grams and the velocity of the club head is 45 meters/second.

a. Find the maximum range at 32°F in meters and convert it to yards (1 m = 1.093 yds). Round your answers to the nearest whole number. **211 yd**

b. Find the maximum range at 80°F in meters and yards to the nearest whole number. **219.72 m; 240 yd**

c. Why might a golfer want to buy a battery-heated glove to keep spare golf balls warm? **Increasing the temperature of the ball appears to increase the distance the ball can travel.**

11-1

Enrichment

Student Edition
Pages 611–617

Translating Quadratic Graphs

When a figure is moved to a new position without undergoing any rotation, then the figure is said to have been **translated** to the new position.

The graph of a quadratic equation in the form $y = (x - b)^2 + c$ is a translation of the graph of $y = x^2$.

Start with $y = x^2$.
Slide to the right 4 units.
$$y = (x - 4)^2$$
Then slide up 3 units.
$$y = (x - 4)^2 + 3$$

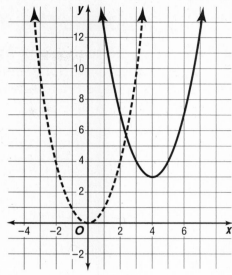

These equations have the form $y = x^2 + c$. Graph each equation.

1. $y = x^2 + 1$

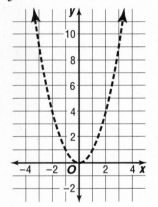

2. $y = x^2 + 2$

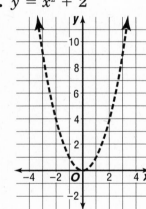

3. $y = x^2 - 2$

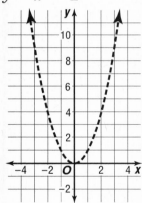

These equations have the form $y = (x - b)^2$. Graph each equation.

4. $y = (x - 1)^2$

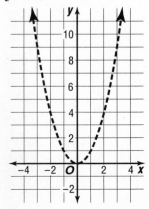

5. $y = (x - 3)^2$

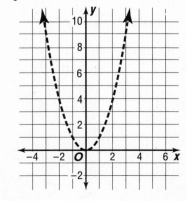

6. $y = (x + 2)^2$

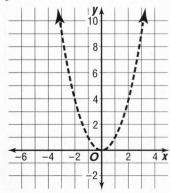

Algebra 1

Enrichment

Translating Quadratic Graphs

When a figure is moved to a new position without undergoing any rotation, then the figure is said to have been **translated** to the new position.

The graph of a quadratic equation in the form $y = (x - b)^2 + c$ is a translation of the graph of $y = x^2$.

Start with $y = x^2$.
Slide to the right 4 units.
$$y = (x - 4)^2$$
Then slide up 3 units.
$$y = (x - 4)^2 + 3$$

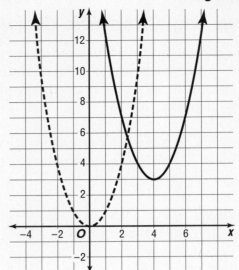

These equations have the form $y = x^2 + c$. Graph each equation.

1. $y = x^2 + 1$

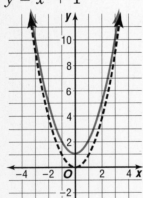

2. $y = x^2 + 2$

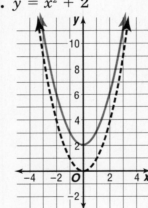

3. $y = x^2 - 2$

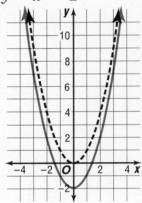

These equations have the form $y = (x - b)^2$. Graph each equation.

4. $y = (x - 1)^2$

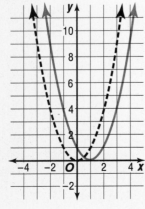

5. $y = (x - 3)^2$

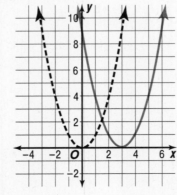

6. $y = (x + 2)^2$

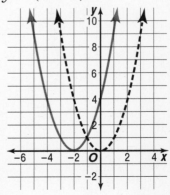

Algebra 1

NAME_____   DATE _____

Enrichment

Mechanical Constructions of Parabolas

A given line and a point determine a parabola. Here is one way to construct the curve.

Use a right triangle *ABC* (or a stiff piece of rectangular cardboard).

Place one leg of the triangle on the given line *d*. Fasten one end of a string with length *BC* at the given point *F* and the other end to the triangle at point *B*.

Put the tip of a pencil at point *P* and keep the string tight.

As you move the triangle along the line *d*, the point of your pencil will trace a parabola.

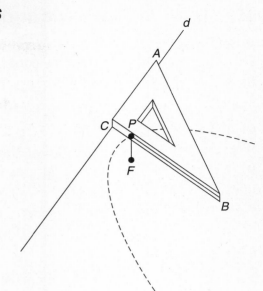

Draw the parabola determined by line d and point F.

1. _____ *d*   **2.**

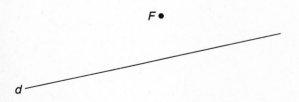

F •

3.   **4.**

F •

F •

5. Use your drawings to complete this conclusion. The greater the distance of point *F* from line *d*,

_____

Mechanical Constructions of Parabolas

A given line and a point determine a parabola. Here is one way to construct the curve.

Use a right triangle ABC (or a stiff piece of rectangular cardboard).

Place one leg of the triangle on the given line d. Fasten one end of a string with length BC at the given point F and the other end to the triangle at point B.

Put the tip of a pencil at point P and keep the string tight.

As you move the triangle along the line d, the point of your pencil will trace a parabola.

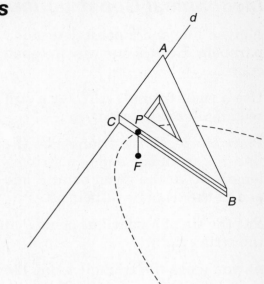

Draw the parabola determined by line d and point F.

1.

2.

3.

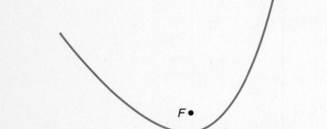

4.

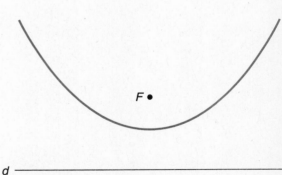

5. Use your drawings to complete this conclusion. The greater the distance of point F from line d,

the wider the opening of the parabola.

Algebra 1

11-3

Enrichment

Odd Numbers and Parabolas

The solid parabola and the dashed stair-step graph are related. The parabola intersects the stair steps at their inside corners.

Use the figure for Exercises 1–3.

1. What is the equation of the parabola?

2. Describe the horizontal sections of the stair-step graph.

3. Describe the vertical sections of the stair-step graph.

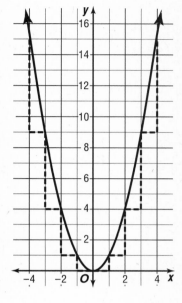

Use the second figure for Exercises 4–6.

4. What is the equation of the parabola?

5. Describe the horizontal sections of the stair steps.

6. Describe the vertical sections.

7. How does the graph of $y = \frac{1}{2}x^2$ relate to the sequence of numbers $\frac{1}{2}, \frac{3}{2}, \frac{5}{2}, \frac{7}{2}, \cdots$?

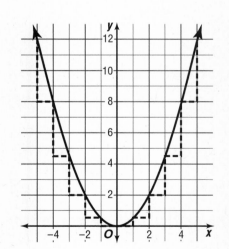

8. Complete this conclusion. To graph a parabola with the equation $y = ax^2$, start at the vertex. Then go over 1 and up a; over 1 and up $3a$;

_____

_____

_____

11-3

Enrichment

Odd Numbers and Parabolas

The solid parabola and the dashed stair-step graph
are related. The parabola intersects the stair steps at
their inside corners.

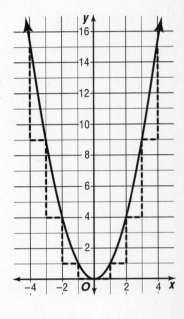

Use the figure for Exercises 1–3.

1. What is the equation of the parabola?
$y = x^2$

2. Describe the horizontal sections of the stair-step
graph.
Each is 1 unit wide.

3. Describe the vertical sections of the stair-step
graph.
They form the sequence 1, 3, 5, 7.

Use the second figure for Exercises 4–6.

4. What is the equation of the parabola?
$y = \dfrac{1}{2}x^2$

5. Describe the horizontal sections of the stair steps.
Each is 1 unit wide.

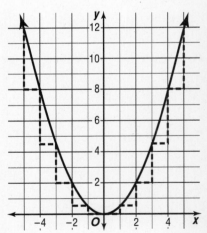

6. Describe the vertical sections.
They form the sequence $\dfrac{1}{2}, \dfrac{3}{2}, \dfrac{5}{2}, \dfrac{7}{2}, \dfrac{9}{2}$.

7. How does the graph of $y = \dfrac{1}{2}x^2$ relate to the
sequence of numbers $\dfrac{1}{2}, \dfrac{3}{2}, \dfrac{5}{2}, \dfrac{7}{2}, \ldots$?
**If the x-values increase by 1, the y-values
increase by the numbers in the sequence.**

8. Complete this conclusion. To graph a parabola
with the equation $y = ax^2$, start at the vertex.
Then go over 1 and up a; over 1 and up $3a$;

over 1 and up 5a; over 1 and up 7a; _____

and so on. The coefficients of a are _____

the odd numbers. _____

T77

NAME_____ DATE _____

Enrichment

Parabolas Through Three Given Points

If you know two points on a straight line, you can find the equation of the line. To find the equation of a parabola, you need three points on the curve.

For example, here is how to approximate an equation of the parabola through the points $(0, -2)$, $(3, 0)$, and $(5, 2)$.

Use the general equation $y = ax^2 + bx + c$. By substituting the given values for x and y, you get three equations.

$(0, -2)$: $-2 = c$
$(3, 0)$: $0 = 9a + 3b + c$
$(5, 2)$: $2 = 25a + 5b + c$

First, substitute -2 for c in the second and third equations. Then solve those two equations as you would any system of two equations. Multiply the second equation by 5 and the third equation by -3.

$$
\begin{aligned}
0 &= 45a + 15b - 10 \\
\underline{-6} &= \underline{-75a - 15b + 6} \\
-6 &= -30a - 15b - 4 \\
a &= \frac{1}{15}
\end{aligned}
$$

To find b, substitute $\frac{1}{15}$ for a in either the second or third equation.

$$
\begin{aligned}
0 &= 9\left(\frac{1}{15}\right) + 3b - 2 \\
b &= \frac{7}{15}
\end{aligned}
$$

The equation of a parabola through the three points is
$y = \frac{1}{15}x^2 + \frac{7}{15}x - 2$.

Find the equation of a parabola through each set of three points.

1. $(1, 5)$, $(0, 6)$, $(2, 3)$

2. $(-5, 0)$, $(0, 0)$, $(8, 100)$

3. $(4, -4)$, $(0, 1)$, $(3, -2)$

4. $(1, 3)$, $(6, 0)$, $(0, 0)$

5. $(2, 2)$, $(5, -3)$, $(0, -1)$

6. $(0, 4)$, $(4, 0)$, $(-4, 4)$

11-4

Enrichment

Parabolas Through Three Given Points

If you know two points on a straight line, you can find the equation of the line. To find the equation of a parabola, you need three points on the curve.

For example, here is how to approximate an equation of the parabola through the points $(0, -2)$, $(3, 0)$, and $(5, 2)$.

Use the general equation $y = ax^2 + bx + c$. By substituting the given values for x and y, you get three equations.

$(0, -2)$: $-2 = c$
$(3, 0)$: $0 = 9a + 3b + c$
$(5, 2)$: $2 = 25a + 5b + c$

First, substitute -2 for c in the second and third equations. Then solve those two equations as you would any system of two equations. Multiply the second equation by 5 and the third equation by -3.

$$\begin{array}{rl} 0 = & 45a + 15b - 10 \\ -6 = & -75a - 15b + 6 \\ \hline -6 = & -30a \qquad - 4 \\ a = & \dfrac{1}{15} \end{array}$$

To find b, substitute $\dfrac{1}{15}$ for a in either the second or third equation.

$$0 = 9\left(\dfrac{1}{15}\right) + 3b - 2$$
$$b = \dfrac{7}{15}$$

The equation of a parabola through the three points is

$$y = \dfrac{1}{15}x^2 + \dfrac{7}{15}x - 2.$$

Find the equation of a parabola through each set of three points.

1. $(1, 5)$, $(0, 6)$, $(2, 3)$
$$y = -\dfrac{1}{2}x^2 - \dfrac{1}{2}x + 6$$

2. $(-5, 0)$, $(0, 0)$, $(8, 100)$
$$y = \dfrac{25}{26}x^2 + \dfrac{125}{26}x$$

3. $(4, -4)$, $(0, 1)$, $(3, -2)$
$$y = -\dfrac{1}{4}x^2 - \dfrac{1}{4}x + 1$$

4. $(1, 3)$, $(6, 0)$, $(0, 0)$
$$y = -\dfrac{3}{5}x^2 + \dfrac{18}{5}x$$

5. $(2, 2)$, $(5, -3)$, $(0, -1)$
$$y = -\dfrac{19}{30}x^2 + \dfrac{83}{30}x - 1$$

6. $(0, 4)$, $(4, 0)$, $(-4, 4)$
$$y = \dfrac{1}{8}x^2 - \dfrac{1}{2}x + 4$$

Enrichment

Perfect, Excessive, Defective, and Amicable Numbers

A **perfect number** is the sum of all of its factors except itself.
Here is an example.

$28 = 1 + 2 + 4 + 7 + 14$

There are very few perfect numbers. Most numbers are either
defective or *excessive*.

An **excessive number** is greater than the sum of all of its
factors except itself.

A **defective number** is less than this sum.

Two numbers are **amicable** if the sum of the factors of the first
number, except for the number itself, equals the second number,
and vice versa.

Solve each problem.

1. Write the perfect numbers between 0 and 31.

2. Write the excessive numbers between 0 and 31.

3. Write the defective numbers between 0 and 31.

4. Show that 8128 is a perfect number.

5. The sum of the reciprocals of all the factors of a perfect
number (including the number itself) equals 2. Show that
this is true for the first two perfect numbers.

6. More than 1000 pairs of amicable numbers have been found.
One member of the first pair is 220. Find the other member.

7. One member of the second pair of amicable numbers is 2620.
Find the other member.

8. The Greek mathematician Euclid proved that the expression
$2^{n-1}(2^n - 1)$ equals a perfect number if the expression inside
the parentheses is prime. Use Euclid's expression with n
equal to 19 to find the seventh perfect number.

Perfect, Excessive, Defective, and Amicable Numbers

A **perfect number** is the sum of all of its factors except itself.
Here is an example.

$$28 = 1 + 2 + 4 + 7 + 14$$

There are very few perfect numbers. Most numbers are either
defective or *excessive*.

An **excessive number** is greater than the sum of all of its
factors except itself.

A **defective number** is less than this sum.

Two numbers are **amicable** if the sum of the factors of the first
number, except for the number itself, equals the second number,
and vice versa.

Solve each problem.

1. Write the perfect numbers between 0 and 31.
   6, 28

2. Write the excessive numbers between 0 and 31. **2, 3, 4, 5, 7, 8, 9, 10, 11, 13, 14,
   15, 16, 17, 19, 21, 22, 23, 25, 26, 27, 29**

3. Write the defective numbers between 0 and 31.
   12, 18, 20, 24, 30

4. Show that 8128 is a perfect number. **8128 = 1 + 2 + 4 + 8 + 16 + 32 + 64
   + 127 + 254 + 508 + 1016 + 2032 + 4064**

5. The sum of the reciprocals of all the factors of a perfect
   number (including the number itself) equals 2. Show that
   this is true for the first two perfect numbers.
   $$\frac{1}{1} + \frac{1}{2} + \frac{1}{3} + \frac{1}{6} = \frac{12}{6} = 2 \qquad \frac{1}{1} + \frac{1}{2} + \frac{1}{4} + \frac{1}{7} + \frac{1}{14} + \frac{1}{28} = \frac{56}{28} = 2$$

6. More than 1000 pairs of amicable numbers have been found.
   One member of the first pair is 220. Find the other member.
   284

7. One member of the second pair of amicable numbers is 2620.
   Find the other member.
   2924

8. The Greek mathematician Euclid proved that the expression
   $2^{n-1}(2^n - 1)$ equals a perfect number if the expression inside
   the parentheses is prime. Use Euclid's expression with n
   equal to 19 to find the seventh perfect number.
   $2^{18}(2^{19} - 1) = 137,438,691,328$

Enrichment

Continued Fractions

The following is an example of a continued fraction. By starting at the bottom you can simplify the expression to a rational number.

$$3 + \cfrac{4}{1 + \cfrac{6}{7}} = 3 + \cfrac{4}{\cfrac{13}{7}}$$

$$= 3 + \cfrac{28}{13} \text{ or } \cfrac{67}{13}$$

Example: Express $\dfrac{48}{19}$ as a continued fraction.

$$\frac{48}{19} = 2 + \frac{10}{19}$$

Notice that the numerator of the last fraction must be equal to 1 before the process stops.

$$= 2 + \cfrac{1}{\cfrac{19}{10}}$$

$$= 2 + \cfrac{1}{1 + \cfrac{9}{10}}$$

$$= 2 + \cfrac{1}{1 + \cfrac{1}{\cfrac{10}{9}}}$$

$$= 2 + \cfrac{1}{1 + \cfrac{1}{1 + \cfrac{1}{9}}}$$

Write each continued fraction as a rational number.

1. $6 + \cfrac{1}{1 + \cfrac{1}{3 + \cfrac{1}{3}}}$

2. $5 + \cfrac{7}{2 + \cfrac{3}{4 + \cfrac{2}{3}}}$

Write each rational number as a continued fraction.

3. $\dfrac{97}{17}$

4. $\dfrac{22}{65}$

Enrichment

Continued Fractions

The following is an example of a continued fraction. By starting at the bottom you can simplify the expression to a rational number.

$$3 + \dfrac{4}{1 + \dfrac{6}{7}} = 3 + \dfrac{4}{\dfrac{13}{7}}$$

$$= 3 + \dfrac{28}{13} \text{ or } \dfrac{67}{13}$$

Example: Express $\dfrac{48}{19}$ as a continued fraction.

$$\dfrac{48}{19} = 2 + \dfrac{10}{19}$$

Notice that the numerator of the last fraction must be equal to 1 before the process stops.

$$= 2 + \dfrac{1}{\dfrac{19}{10}}$$

$$= 2 + \dfrac{1}{1 + \dfrac{9}{10}}$$

$$= 2 + \dfrac{1}{1 + \dfrac{1}{\dfrac{10}{9}}}$$

$$= 2 + \dfrac{1}{1 + \dfrac{1}{1 + \dfrac{1}{9}}}$$

Write each continued fraction as a rational number.

1. $6 + \dfrac{1}{1 + \dfrac{1}{3 + \dfrac{1}{3}}}$ $\dfrac{88}{13}$

2. $5 + \dfrac{7}{2 + \dfrac{3}{4 + \dfrac{2}{3}}}$ $\dfrac{283}{37}$

Write each rational number as a continued fraction.

3. $\dfrac{97}{17}$ $5 + \dfrac{1}{1 + \dfrac{1}{2 + \dfrac{1}{2 + \dfrac{1}{2}}}}$

4. $\dfrac{22}{65}$ $\dfrac{1}{2 + \dfrac{1}{1 + \dfrac{1}{21}}}$

Enrichment

Surface Area of Solid Figures

Many solid objects are formed by rectangles and squares. A box is an example.

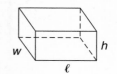

The dimensions of the box shown at the right are represented by letters. The length of the base is ℓ units, its width is w units, and the height of the box is h units.

Suppose the box is cut on the seams so that it can be spread out on a flattened surface as shown at the right. The area of this figure is the surface area of the box. Find a formula for the surface area of the box.

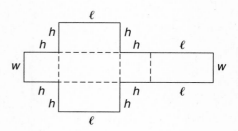

There are 6 rectangles in the figure. The surface area is the sum of the areas of the 6 rectangles.

$$S = hw + h\ell + \ell w + h\ell + hw + \ell w$$
$$S = 2\ell w + 2h\ell + 2hw$$

Find the surface area of a box with the given dimensions.

1. $\ell = 14$ cm, $w = 8$ cm, $h = 2$ cm

2. $\ell = 40$ cm, $w = 30$ cm, $h = 25$ cm

3. $\ell = x$ cm, $w = (x - 3)$ cm, $h = (x + 3)$ cm

4. $\ell = (s + 9)$ cm, $w = (s - 9)$ cm, $h = (s + 9)$ cm

5. The surface area of a box is 142 cm². The length of the base is 2 cm longer than its width. The height of the box is 2 cm less than the width of the base. Find the dimensions of the box.

6. Write an expression that represents the surface area of the figure shown at the right. Include the surface area of the base.

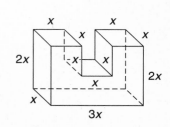

Surface Area of Solid Figures

Many solid objects are formed by rectangles and squares. A box is an example.

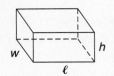

The dimensions of the box shown at the right are represented by letters. The length of the base is ℓ units, its width is w units, and the height of the box is h units.

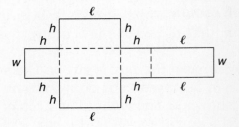

Suppose the box is cut on the seams so that it can be spread out on a flattened surface as shown at the right. The area of this figure is the surface area of the box. Find a formula for the surface area of the box.

There are 6 rectangles in the figure. The surface area is the sum of the areas of the 6 rectangles.

$$S = hw + h\ell + \ell w + h\ell + hw + \ell w$$
$$S = 2\ell w + 2h\ell + 2hw$$

Find the surface area of a box with the given dimensions.

1. $\ell = 14$ cm, $w = 8$ cm, $h = 2$ cm
312 cm²

2. $\ell = 40$ cm, $w = 30$ cm, $h = 25$ cm
5900 cm²

3. $\ell = x$ cm, $w = (x - 3)$ cm,
$h = (x + 3)$ cm **6($x^2 - 3$) cm²**

4. $\ell = (s + 9)$ cm, $w = (s - 9)$ cm,
$h = (s + 9)$ cm
($6s^2 + 36s - 162$) cm²

5. The surface area of a box is 142 cm². The length of the base is 2 cm longer than its width. The height of the box is 2 cm less than the width of the base. Find the dimensions of the box.
$h = x = 3$ cm; $w = x + 2 = 5$ cm; $\ell = x + 4 = 7$ cm

6. Write an expression that represents the surface area of the figure shown at the right. Include the surface area of the base. **$22x^2$**

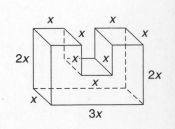

Enrichment

Synthetic Division

You can divide a polynomial such as $3x^3 - 4x^2 - 3x - 2$ by a binomial such as $x - 3$ by a process called **synthetic division**. Compare the process with long division in the following explanation.

Example: Divide $(3x^3 - 4x^2 - 3x - 2)$ by $(x - 3)$ using synthetic division.

1. Show the coefficients of the terms in descending order.
2. The divisor is $x - 3$. Since 3 is to be subtracted, write 3 in the corner ⌐.
3. Bring down the first coefficient, 3.
4. Multiply. $3 \cdot 3 = 9$
5. Add. $-4 + 9 = 5$
6. Multiply. $3 \cdot 5 = 15$
7. Add. $-3 + 15 = 12$
8. Multiply. $3 \cdot 12 = 36$
9. Add. $-2 + 36 = 34$

$$
\begin{array}{r|rrrr}
 & 3 & -4 & -3 & -2 \\
 &   & 9 & 15 & 36 \\
\hline
3 & 3 & 5 & 12 & 34
\end{array}
$$

$3x^2 + 5x + 12$, remainder 34

Check: Use long division.

$$
\begin{array}{r}
3x^2 + 5x + 12 \\
x - 3 \overline{)3x^3 - 4x^2 - 3x - 2} \\
\underline{3x^3 - 9x^2} \\
5x^2 - 3x \\
\underline{5x^2 - 15x} \\
12x - 2 \\
\underline{12x - 36} \\
34
\end{array}
$$

The result is $3x^2 + 5x + 12 + \dfrac{34}{x - 3}$.

Divide by using synthetic division. Check your result using long division.

1. $(x^3 + 6x^2 + 3x + 1) \div (x - 2)$

2. $(x^3 - 3x^2 - 6x - 20) \div (x - 5)$

3. $(2x^3 - 5x + 1) \div (x + 1)$

4. $(3x^3 - 7x^2 + 4) \div (x - 2)$

5. $(x^3 + 2x^2 - x + 4) \div (x + 3)$

6. $(x^3 + 4x^2 - 3x - 11) \div (x - 4)$

Enrichment

Synthetic Division

You can divide a polynomial such as $3x^3 - 4x^2 - 3x - 2$ by a binomial such as $x - 3$ by a process called **synthetic division.** Compare the process with long division in the following explanation.

Example: Divide $(3x^3 - 4x^2 - 3x - 2)$ by $(x - 3)$ using synthetic division.

1. Show the coefficients of the terms in descending order.
2. The divisor is $x - 3$. Since 3 is to be subtracted, write 3 in the corner ⌐.
3. Bring down the first coefficient, 3.
4. Multiply. $3 \cdot 3 = 9$
5. Add. $-4 + 9 = 5$
6. Multiply. $3 \cdot 5 = 15$
7. Add. $-3 + 15 = 12$
8. Multiply. $3 \cdot 12 = 36$
9. Add. $-2 + 36 = 34$

$$
\begin{array}{c|rrrr}
 & 3 & -4 & -3 & -2 \\
 &   & 9 & 15 & 36 \\
\hline
3 & 3 & 5 & 12 & 34
\end{array}
$$

$3x^2 + 5x + 12$, remainder 34

Check: Use long division.

$$
\begin{array}{r}
3x^2 + 5x + 12 \\
x - 3 \overline{)3x^3 - 4x^2 - 3x - 2} \\
\underline{3x^3 - 9x^2} \\
5x^2 - 3x \\
\underline{5x^2 - 15x} \\
12x - 2 \\
\underline{12x - 36} \\
34
\end{array}
$$

The result is $3x^2 + 5x + 12 + \dfrac{34}{x - 3}$.

Divide by using synthetic division. Check your result using long division.

1. $(x^3 + 6x^2 + 3x + 1) \div (x - 2)$
   $x^2 + 8x + 19 + \dfrac{39}{x - 2}$

2. $(x^3 - 3x^2 - 6x - 20) \div (x - 5)$
   $x^2 + 2x + 4$

3. $(2x^3 - 5x + 1) \div (x + 1)$
   $2x^2 - 2x - 3 + \dfrac{4}{x + 1}$

4. $(3x^3 - 7x^2 + 4) \div (x - 2)$
   $3x^2 - x - 2$

5. $(x^3 + 2x^2 - x + 4) \div (x + 3)$
   $x^2 - x + 2 - \dfrac{2}{x + 3}$

6. $(x^3 + 4x^2 - 3x - 11) \div (x - 4)$
   $x^2 + 8x + 29 + \dfrac{105}{x - 4}$

Algebra 1

12-4

Enrichment

Golden Rectangles

A **golden rectangle** has the property
that its sides satisfy the following
proportion.

$$\frac{a + b}{a} = \frac{a}{b}$$

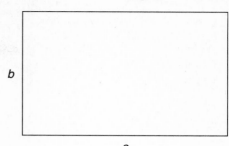

Two quadratic equations can be written from the proportion.
These are sometimes called **golden quadratic** equations.

1. In the proportion, let $a = 1$. Use
cross-multiplication to write a
quadratic equation.

2. Solve the equation in problem 1
for b.

3. In the proportion, let $b = 1$. Write a
quadratic equation in a.

4. Solve the equation in problem 3
for a.

5. Explain why $\frac{1}{2}(\sqrt{5} + 1)$ and $\frac{1}{2}(\sqrt{5} - 1)$ are called golden ratios.

Another property of golden rectangles is that a square drawn
inside a golden rectangle creates another, smaller golden
rectangle.

In the design at the right,
opposite vertices of each
square have been connected
with quarters of circles.

For example, the arc from
point B to point C is
created by putting the
point of a compass at point
A. The radius of the arc is
the length BA.

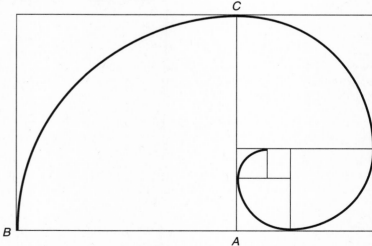

6. On a separate sheet of paper, draw a larger version of the
design. Start with a golden rectangle with a long side of
10 inches.

Golden Rectangles

A **golden rectangle** has the property
that its sides satisfy the following
proportion.

$$\frac{a + b}{a} = \frac{a}{b}$$

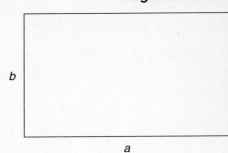

Two quadratic equations can be written from the proportion.
These are sometimes called **golden quadratic** equations.

1. In the proportion, let $a = 1$. Use
cross-multiplication to write a
quadratic equation.
$b^2 + b - 1 = 0$

2. Solve the equation in problem 1
for b.

$b = \dfrac{-1 + \sqrt{5}}{2}$

3. In the proportion, let $b = 1$. Write a
quadratic equation in a.
$a^2 - a - 1 = 0$

4. Solve the equation in problem 3
for a.

$a = \dfrac{1 + \sqrt{5}}{2}$

5. Explain why $\frac{1}{2}(\sqrt{5} + 1)$ and $\frac{1}{2}(\sqrt{5} - 1)$ are called golden ratios.

**They are the ratios of the sides in a golden
rectangle. The first is the ratio of the long
side to the short side; the second is short
side: long side.**

Another property of golden rectangles is that a square drawn
inside a golden rectangle creates another, smaller golden
rectangle.

In the design at the right,
opposite vertices of each
square have been connected
with quarters of circles.

For example, the arc from
point B to point C is
created by putting the
point of a compass at point
A. The radius of the arc is
the length BA.

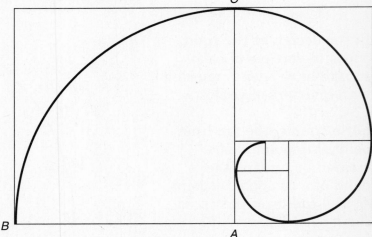

6. On a separate sheet of paper, draw a larger version of the
design. Start with a golden rectangle with a long side of
10 inches.

The short side should be about $6\frac{3}{16}$ inches.

NAME_____ DATE _____

Enrichment

Sum and Difference of Any Two Like Powers

The sum of any two like powers can be written $a^n + b^n$, where n is a positive integer. The difference of like powers is $a^n - b^n$. Under what conditions are these expressions exactly divisible by $(a + b)$ or $(a - b)$? The answer depends on whether n is an odd or even number.

Use long division to find the following quotients. (HINT: Write $a^3 + b^3$ as $a^3 + 0a^2 + 0a + b^3$.) Is the numerator exactly divisible by the denominator? Write yes or no.

1. $\dfrac{a^3 + b^3}{a + b}$

2. $\dfrac{a^3 + b^3}{a - b}$

3. $\dfrac{a^3 - b^3}{a + b}$

4. $\dfrac{a^3 - b^3}{a - b}$

5. $\dfrac{a^4 + b^4}{a + b}$

6. $\dfrac{a^4 + b^4}{a - b}$

7. $\dfrac{a^4 - b^4}{a + b}$

8. $\dfrac{a^4 - b^4}{a - b}$

9. $\dfrac{a^5 + b^5}{a + b}$

10. $\dfrac{a^5 + b^5}{a - b}$

11. $\dfrac{a^5 - b^5}{a + b}$

12. $\dfrac{a^5 - b^5}{a - b}$

13. Use the words *odd* and *even* to complete these two statements.

 a. $a^n + b^n$ is divisible by $a + b$ if n is _____, and by neither

 $a + b$ nor $a - b$ if n is _____.

 b. $a^n - b^n$ is divisible by $a - b$ if n is _____, and by both

 $a + b$ and $a - b$ if n is _____.

14. Describe the signs of the terms of the quotients when the divisor is $a - b$.

15. Describe the signs of the terms of the quotient when the divisor is $a + b$.

Algebra 1

Enrichment

Sum and Difference of Any Two Like Powers

The sum of any two like powers can be written $a^n + b^n$, where n is a positive integer. The difference of like powers is $a^n - b^n$. Under what conditions are these expressions exactly divisible by $(a + b)$ or $(a - b)$? The answer depends on whether n is an odd or even number.

Use long division to find the following quotients. (HINT: Write $a^3 + b^3$ as $a^3 + 0a^2 + 0a + b^3$.) Is the numerator exactly divisible by the denominator? Write <u>yes</u> or <u>no</u>.

1. $\dfrac{a^3 + b^3}{a + b}$

   yes

2. $\dfrac{a^3 + b^3}{a - b}$

   no

3. $\dfrac{a^3 - b^3}{a + b}$

   no

4. $\dfrac{a^3 - b^3}{a - b}$

   yes

5. $\dfrac{a^4 + b^4}{a + b}$

   no

6. $\dfrac{a^4 + b^4}{a - b}$

   no

7. $\dfrac{a^4 - b^4}{a + b}$

   yes

8. $\dfrac{a^4 - b^4}{a - b}$

   yes

9. $\dfrac{a^5 + b^5}{a + b}$

   yes

10. $\dfrac{a^5 + b^5}{a - b}$

    no

11. $\dfrac{a^5 - b^5}{a + b}$

    no

12. $\dfrac{a^5 - b^5}{a - b}$

    yes

13. Use the words *odd* and *even* to complete these two statements.

    a. $a^n + b^n$ is divisible by $a + b$ if n is __odd__, and by neither $a + b$ nor $a - b$ if n is __even__.

    b. $a^n - b^n$ is divisible by $a - b$ if n is __odd__, and by both $a + b$ and $a - b$ if n is __even__.

14. Describe the signs of the terms of the quotients when the divisor is $a - b$.
    The terms are all positive.

15. Describe the signs of the terms of the quotient when the divisor is $a + b$.
    The terms are alternately positive and negative.

Enrichment

The Work Problem and Similar Right Triangles

"The work problem" has been included in algebra textbooks for a very long time. In older books, the people in the problem always seemed to be digging ditches.

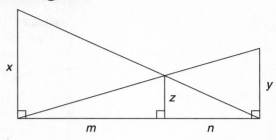

If Olivia can dig a ditch in x hours and George can dig the same ditch in y hours, how long will it take them to dig the ditch if they work together?

You have learned a way to solve this type of problem using rational equations. It can also be solved using a geometric model that uses two overlapping right triangles.

In the drawing, the length x is Olivia's time. The length y is George's time. The answer to the problem is the length of the segment z. The distance $m + n$ can be any convenient length.

Solve each problem.

1. Solve the work problem for $x = 6$ and $y = 3$ by drawing a diagram and measuring.

2. Confirm your solution to problem 1 by writing and solving a rational equation.

3. On a separate sheet of paper, create a word problem to go with the values $x = 6$ and $y = 3$.

4. On a separate sheet of paper, solve this problem with a diagram. Use centimeters and measure to the nearest tenth. Olivia can wash a car in 3 hours. George can wash a car in 4 hours. How long will it take them working together to wash one car?

5. Triangles that have the same shape are called *similar triangles*. You may have learned that corresponding sides of similar triangles form equal ratios. Using the drawing at the top of the page, you can thus conclude that Equations A and B below are true. Use the equations to prove the formula for the work problem.

Equation A

$$\frac{z}{x} = \frac{n}{m + n}$$

Equation B

$$\frac{z}{y} = \frac{m}{m + n}$$

Work Formula

$$\frac{1}{x} + \frac{1}{y} = \frac{1}{z}$$

Algebra 1

Enrichment

The Work Problem and Similar Right Triangles

"The work problem" has been included in algebra textbooks for a very long time. In older books, the people in the problem always seemed to be digging ditches.

If Olivia can dig a ditch in x hours and George can dig the same ditch in y hours, how long will it take them to dig the ditch if they work together?

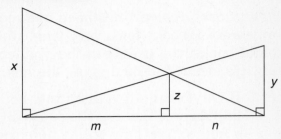

You have learned a way to solve this type of problem using rational equations. It can also be solved using a geometric model that uses two overlapping right triangles.

In the drawing, the length x is Olivia's time. The length y is George's time. The answer to the problem is the length of the segment z. The distance $m + n$ can be any convenient length.

**1 h = 0.5 cm
Students' scales
will vary.**

Solve each problem.   **1. z = 2 hours**

1. Solve the work problem for $x = 6$ and $y = 3$ by drawing a diagram and measuring.

2. Confirm your solution to problem 1 by writing and solving a rational equation.

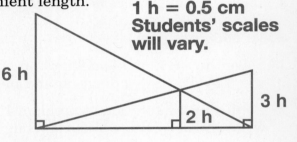

3. On a separate sheet of paper, create a word problem to go with the values $x = 6$ and $y = 3$. **Answers will vary.**

2. $\dfrac{t}{6} + \dfrac{t}{3} = 1$ or

$\dfrac{1}{6} + \dfrac{1}{3} = \dfrac{1}{t}$; $t = 2$

4. On a separate sheet of paper, solve this problem with a diagram. Use centimeters and measure to the nearest tenth. Olivia can wash a car in 3 hours. George can wash a car in 4 hours. How long will it take them working together to wash one car? **about 1.7 hours**

5. Triangles that have the same shape are called *similar triangles*. You may have learned that corresponding sides of similar triangles form equal ratios. Using the drawing at the top of the page, you can thus conclude that Equations A and B below are true. Use the equations to prove the formula for the work problem.

Equation A   **Equation B**   **Work Formula**

$\dfrac{z}{x} = \dfrac{n}{m + n}$ $\dfrac{z}{y} = \dfrac{m}{m + n}$ $\dfrac{1}{x} + \dfrac{1}{y} = \dfrac{1}{z}$

Adding equations A and B gives $\dfrac{z}{x} + \dfrac{z}{y} = \dfrac{m + n}{m + n}$. **So,** $\dfrac{z}{x} + \dfrac{z}{y} = 1$.

Dividing both sides by z gives $\dfrac{1}{x} + \dfrac{1}{y} = \dfrac{1}{z}$.

Algebra 1

Enrichment

Complex Fractions

Complex fractions are really not complicated. Remember that a fraction can be interpreted as dividing the numerator by the denominator.

$$\frac{\frac{2}{3}}{\frac{5}{7}} = \frac{2}{3} \div \frac{5}{7} = \frac{2}{3} \cdot \frac{7}{5} = \frac{2(7)}{3(5)} = \frac{14}{15}$$

Let a, b, c, and d be numbers, with $b \neq 0$, $c \neq 0$, and $d \neq 0$.

$$\frac{\frac{a}{b}}{\frac{c}{d}} = \frac{a}{b} \div \frac{c}{d} = \frac{a}{b} \cdot \frac{d}{c} = \frac{a\,d}{bc}$$

Notice the pattern:

numerator of the answer (ad) $\quad \begin{array}{c} \frac{a}{b} \\ \frac{c}{d} \end{array}$ denominator of the answer (bc)

Example 1: Simplify $\dfrac{\frac{5x}{4}}{\frac{x+2}{3}}$.

$$\frac{\frac{5x}{4}}{\frac{x+2}{3}} = \frac{5x(3)}{4(x+2)}$$

$$= \frac{15x}{4x+8}$$

Example 2: Simplify $\dfrac{\frac{x}{2}+4}{3x-2}$.

$$\frac{\frac{x}{2}+4}{3x-2} = \frac{\frac{x+8}{2}}{\frac{3x-2}{1}}$$

$$= \frac{(x+8)(1)}{2(3x-2)} = \frac{x+8}{6x-4}$$

Simplify each complex fraction.

1. $\dfrac{\frac{2x}{5}}{\frac{y}{6}}$

2. $\dfrac{\frac{4}{5x}}{\frac{3}{x}}$

3. $\dfrac{x-3}{\frac{2x+1}{4}}$

4. $\dfrac{x^2+\frac{1}{3}}{4x+\frac{1}{3}}$

5. $\dfrac{1-x^{-1}}{\frac{2x}{5}-1}$

6. $\dfrac{x+2x^{-2}}{2+\frac{x}{3}}$

7. $\dfrac{x}{x+\dfrac{1}{x+\frac{1}{x}}}$

8. $\dfrac{x+2}{x-2+\dfrac{1}{x+2+\frac{1}{x}}}$

Algebra 1

12-7

NAME_____

DATE _____

Enrichment

Student Edition
Pages 691–696

Complex Fractions

Complex fractions are really not complicated. Remember that a fraction can be interpreted as dividing the numerator by the denominator.

$$\frac{\frac{2}{3}}{\frac{5}{7}} = \frac{2}{3} \div \frac{5}{7} = \frac{2}{3} \cdot \frac{7}{5} = \frac{2(7)}{3(5)} = \frac{14}{15}$$

Let a, b, c, and d be numbers, with $b \neq 0$, $c \neq 0$, and $d \neq 0$.

$$\frac{\frac{a}{b}}{\frac{c}{d}} = \frac{a}{b} \div \frac{c}{d} = \frac{a}{b} \cdot \frac{d}{c} = \frac{ad}{bc}$$

Notice the pattern: numerator of the answer (ad) $\begin{bmatrix} \frac{a}{b} \\ \frac{c}{d} \end{bmatrix}$ denominator of the answer (bc)

Example 1: Simplify $\dfrac{\frac{5x}{4}}{\frac{x+2}{3}}$.

$$\frac{\frac{5x}{4}}{\frac{x+2}{3}} = \frac{5x(3)}{4(x+2)}$$

$$= \frac{15x}{4x+8}$$

Example 2: Simplify $\dfrac{\frac{x}{2}+4}{3x-2}$.

$$\frac{\frac{x}{2}+4}{3x-2} = \frac{\frac{x+8}{2}}{\frac{3x-2}{1}}$$

$$= \frac{(x+8)(1)}{2(3x-2)} = \frac{x+8}{6x-4}$$

Simplify each complex fraction.

1. $\dfrac{\frac{2x}{5}}{\frac{y}{6}}$ $\dfrac{12x}{5y}$

2. $\dfrac{\frac{4}{5x}}{\frac{3}{x}}$ $\dfrac{4}{15}$

3. $\dfrac{x-3}{\frac{2x+1}{4}}$ $\dfrac{4x-12}{2x+1}$

4. $\dfrac{x^2 + \frac{1}{3}}{4x + \frac{1}{3}}$ $\dfrac{3x^2+1}{12x+1}$

5. $\dfrac{1 - x^{-1}}{\frac{2x}{5} - 1}$ $\dfrac{5x-5}{2x^2-5x}$

6. $\dfrac{x + 2x^{-2}}{2 + \frac{x}{3}}$ $\dfrac{3(x^3+2)}{x^3+6x^2}$

7. $\dfrac{x}{x + \frac{1}{x + \frac{1}{x}}}$ $\dfrac{x^2+1}{x^2+2}$

8. $\dfrac{x+2}{x-2+\frac{1}{x+2+\frac{1}{x}}}$ $\dfrac{x^3+4x^2+5x+2}{x^3-2x-2}$

Algebra 1

NAME_____ DATE _____

Enrichment

Using Rational Expressions and Equations

In 1985 Steve Cram set a world record for the mile run with a time of 3:46.31. In 1954, Roger Bannister ran the first mile under 4 minutes at 3:59.4. Had they run those times in the same race, how far in front of Bannister would Cram have been at the finish?

Use $\frac{d}{t} = r$. Since 3 min 46.31 s = 226.31 s, and 3 min 59.4 s = 239.4 s, Cram's rate was $\frac{5280 \text{ ft}}{226.31 \text{ s}}$ and Bannister's rate was $\frac{5280 \text{ ft}}{239.4 \text{ s}}$.

	r	t	d
Cram	$\frac{5280}{226.31}$	226.31	5280 feet
Bannister	$\frac{5280}{239.4}$	226.31	$\frac{5280}{239.4} \cdot 226.31$ or 4491.3 feet

Therefore, when Cram hit the tape, he would be 5280 − 4491.3, or 288.7 feet, ahead of Bannister. Let's see whether we can develop a formula for this type of problem.

Let D = the distance raced,
W = the winner's time,
and L = the loser's time.

Following the same pattern, you obtain the results shown in the table at the right.

The winning distance will be $D - \frac{DW}{L}$.

	r	t	d
Winner	$\frac{D}{W}$	W	$\frac{D}{W} \cdot W = D$
Loser	$\frac{D}{L}$	W	$\frac{D}{L} \cdot W = \frac{DW}{L}$

1. Show that the expression for the winning distance is equivalent to $\frac{D(L - W)}{L}$.

Use the formula winning distance $= \frac{D(L - W)}{L}$ to find the winning distance for each of the following Olympic races.

2. women's 400 meter relay: Canada 48.4 s (1928); East Germany 41.6 s (1980)

3. men's 200 meter freestyle swimming: Mark Spitz 1 min 52.78 s (1972); Michael Gross 1 min 47.44 s (1984)

4. men's 50,000 meter walk: Thomas Green 4 h 50 min 10 s (1932); Hartwig Gauter 3 h 49 min 24 s (1980)

5. women's 400 meter freestyle relay: Great Britain 5 min 52.8 s (1912); East Germany 3 min 42.71 s (1980)

Enrichment

Using Rational Expressions and Equations

In 1985 Steve Cram set a world record for the mile run with a time of 3:46.31. In 1954, Roger Bannister ran the first mile under 4 minutes at 3:59.4. Had they run those times in the same race, how far in front of Bannister would Cram have been at the finish?

Use $\frac{d}{t} = r$. Since 3 min 46.31 s = 226.31 s, and 3 min 59.4 s = 239.4 s, Cram's rate was $\frac{5280 \text{ ft}}{226.31 \text{ s}}$ and Bannister's rate was $\frac{5280 \text{ ft}}{239.4 \text{ s}}$.

	r	t	d
Cram	$\frac{5280}{226.31}$	226.31	5280 feet
Bannister	$\frac{5280}{239.4}$	226.31	$\frac{5280}{239.4} \cdot 226.31$ or 4491.3 feet

Therefore, when Cram hit the tape, he would be 5280 − 4491.3, or 288.7 feet, ahead of Bannister. Let's see whether we can develop a formula for this type of problem.

Let D = the distance raced,
W = the winner's time,
and L = the loser's time.

Following the same pattern, you obtain the results shown in the table at the right.

	r	t	d
Winner	$\frac{D}{W}$	W	$\frac{D}{W} \cdot W = D$
Loser	$\frac{D}{L}$	W	$\frac{D}{L} \cdot W = \frac{DW}{L}$

The winning distance will be $D - \frac{DW}{L}$.

1. Show that the expression for the winning distance is equivalent to $\frac{D(L - W)}{L}$.

$$D - \frac{DW}{L} = \frac{DL}{L} - \frac{DW}{L}$$
$$\frac{DL - DW}{L}$$
$$\frac{D(L - W)}{L}$$

Use the formula winning distance = $\frac{D(L - W)}{L}$ to find the winning distance for each of the following Olympic races.

2. women's 400 meter relay: Canada 48.4 s (1928); East Germany 41.6 s (1980) **56.2 meters**

3. men's 200 meter freestyle swimming: Mark Spitz 1 min 52.78 s (1972); Michael Gross 1 min 47.44 s (1984) **9.5 meters**

4. men's 50,000 meter walk: Thomas Green 4 h 50 min 10 s (1932); Hartwig Gauter 3 h 49 min 24 s (1980) **10,471 meters**

5. women's 400 meter freestyle relay: Great Britain 5 min 52.8 s (1912); East Germany 3 min 42.71 s (1980) **147.5 meters**

A Space-Saving Method

Two arrangements for cookies on a 32 cm by 40 cm cookie sheet are shown at the right. The cookies have 8-cm diameters after they are baked. The centers of the cookies are on the vertices of squares in the top arrangement. In the other, the centers are on the vertices of equilateral triangles. Which arrangement is more economical? The triangle arrangement is more economical, because it contains one more cookie.

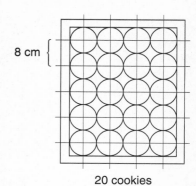

8 cm

20 cookies

In the square arrangement, rows are placed every 8 cm. At what intervals are rows placed in the triangle arrangement?

Look at the right triangle labeled a, b, and c. A leg a of the triangle is the radius of a cookie, or 4 cm. The hypotenuse c is the sum of two radii, or 8 cm. Use the Pythagorean theorem to find b, the interval of the rows.

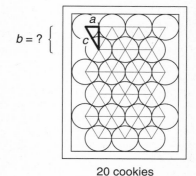

$b = ?$

20 cookies

$$c^2 = a^2 + b^2$$
$$8^2 = 4^2 + b^2$$
$$64 - 16 = b^2$$
$$\sqrt{48} = b$$
$$4\sqrt{3} = b$$
$$b = 4\sqrt{3} \approx 6.93$$

The rows are placed approximately every 6.93 cm.

Solve each problem.

1. Suppose cookies with 10-cm diameters are arranged in the triangular pattern shown above. What is the interval b of the rows?

2. Find the diameter of a cookie if the rows are placed in the triangular pattern every $3\sqrt{3}$ cm.

3. Describe other practical applications in which this kind of triangular pattern can be used to economize on space.

NAME_____ DATE _____

Enrichment

A Space-Saving Method

Two arrangements for cookies on a 32 cm by 40 cm cookie sheet are shown at the right. The cookies have 8-cm diameters after they are baked. The centers of the cookies are on the vertices of squares in the top arrangement. In the other, the centers are on the vertices of equilateral triangles. Which arrangement is more economical? The triangle arrangement is more economical, because it contains one more cookie.

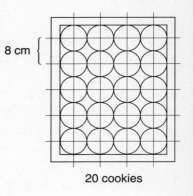

8 cm

20 cookies

In the square arrangement, rows are placed every 8 cm. At what intervals are rows placed in the triangle arrangement?

Look at the right triangle labeled a, b, and c. A leg a of the triangle is the radius of a cookie, or 4 cm. The hypotenuse c is the sum of two radii, or 8 cm. Use the Pythagorean theorem to find b, the interval of the rows.

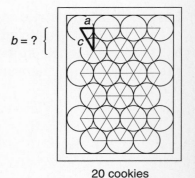

$b = ?$

a

c

20 cookies

$$c^2 = a^2 + b^2$$
$$8^2 = 4^2 + b^2$$
$$64 - 16 = b^2$$
$$\sqrt{48} = b$$
$$4\sqrt{3} = b$$
$$b = 4\sqrt{3} \approx 6.93$$

The rows are placed approximately every 6.93 cm.

Solve each problem.

1. Suppose cookies with 10-cm diameters are arranged in the triangular pattern shown above. What is the interval b of the rows? **8.66 cm**

2. Find the diameter of a cookie if the rows are placed in the triangular pattern every $3\sqrt{3}$ cm. **6 cm**

3. Describe other practical applications in which this kind of triangular pattern can be used to economize on space. **Answers will vary.**

 Algebra 1

Enrichment

Rational Exponents

You have developed the following properties of powers when a is a positive real number and m and n are integers.

$$a^m \cdot a^n = a^{m+n} \qquad (ab)^m = a^m b^m \qquad a^0 = 1$$

$$(a^m)^n = a^{mn} \qquad \frac{a^m}{a^n} = a^{m-n} \qquad a^{-m} = \frac{1}{a^m}$$

Exponents need not be restricted to integers. We can define rational exponents so that operations involving them will be governed by the properties for integer exponents.

$$\left(a^{\frac{1}{2}}\right)^2 = a^{\frac{1}{2} \cdot 2} = a \qquad \left(a^{\frac{1}{3}}\right)^3 = a^{\frac{1}{3} \cdot 3} \qquad \left(a^{\frac{1}{n}}\right)^n = a^{\frac{1}{n} \cdot n} = a$$

$a^{\frac{1}{2}}$ squared is a. $\qquad$ $a^{\frac{1}{3}}$ cubed is a. $\qquad$ $a^{\frac{1}{n}}$ to the n power is a.

$a^{\frac{1}{2}}$ is a square root of a. $\quad$ $a^{\frac{1}{3}}$ is a cube root of a. $\quad$ $a^{\frac{1}{n}}$ is an nth root of a.

$$a^{\frac{1}{2}} = \sqrt{a} \qquad\qquad a^{\frac{1}{3}} = \sqrt[3]{a} \qquad\qquad a^{\frac{1}{n}} = \sqrt[n]{a}$$

Now let us investigate the meaning of $a^{\frac{m}{n}}$.

$$a^{\frac{m}{n}} = a^{m \cdot \frac{1}{n}} (a^m)^{\frac{1}{n}} = \sqrt[n]{a^m} \qquad\qquad a^{\frac{m}{n}} = a^{\frac{1}{n} \cdot m} = \left(a^{\frac{1}{n}}\right)^m = (\sqrt[n]{a})^m$$

Therefore, $a^{\frac{m}{n}} = \sqrt[n]{a^m}$ or $(\sqrt[n]{a})^m$.

Example 1: Write $\sqrt[4]{a^3}$ in exponential form. $\qquad$ **Example 2:** Write $a^{\frac{2}{5}}$ in radical form.

$$\sqrt[4]{a^3} = a^{\frac{3}{4}} \qquad\qquad\qquad a^{\frac{2}{5}} = \sqrt[5]{a^2}$$

Example 3: Find $\dfrac{a^{\frac{2}{3}}}{a^{\frac{1}{2}}}$.

$$\frac{a^{\frac{2}{3}}}{a^{\frac{1}{2}}} = a^{\frac{2}{3} - \frac{1}{2}} = a^{\frac{4}{6} - \frac{3}{6}} = a^{\frac{1}{6}} \text{ or } \sqrt[6]{a}$$

Write each expression in radical form.

1. $b^{\frac{3}{2}}$ $\qquad\qquad$ **2.** $3c^{\frac{1}{2}}$ $\qquad\qquad$ **3.** $(3c)^{\frac{1}{2}}$

Write each expression in exponential form.

4. $\sqrt[3]{b^4}$ $\qquad\qquad$ **5.** $\sqrt{4a^3}$ $\qquad\qquad$ **6.** $2 \cdot \sqrt[3]{b^2}$

Perform the operation indicated. Answers should show positive exponents only.

7. $\left(a^3 b^{\frac{1}{4}}\right)^2$ $\qquad\qquad$ **8.** $\dfrac{-8a^{\frac{3}{4}}}{2a^{\frac{1}{2}}}$ $\qquad\qquad$ **9.** $\left(\dfrac{b^{\frac{1}{2}}}{b^{-\frac{2}{3}}}\right)^3$

10. $\sqrt{a^3} \cdot \sqrt{a}$ $\qquad\qquad$ **11.** $\left(a^2 b^{-\frac{1}{3}}\right)^{-\frac{1}{2}}$ $\qquad\qquad$ **12.** $-2a^{\frac{1}{3}} b^0 \left(5a^{\frac{1}{2}} b^{-\frac{2}{3}}\right)$

Rational Exponents

You have developed the following properties of powers when a is a positive real number and m and n are integers.

$$a^m \cdot a^n = a^{m+n} \qquad (ab)^m = a^m b^m \qquad a^0 = 1$$

$$(a^m)^n = a^{mn} \qquad \frac{a^m}{a^n} = a^{m-n} \qquad a^{-m} = \frac{1}{a^m}$$

Exponents need not be restricted to integers. We can define rational exponents so that operations involving them will be governed by the properties for integer exponents.

$$\left(a^{\frac{1}{2}}\right)^2 = a^{\frac{1}{2} \cdot 2} = a \qquad \left(a^{\frac{1}{3}}\right)^3 = a^{\frac{1}{3} \cdot 3} \qquad \left(a^{\frac{1}{n}}\right)^n = a^{\frac{1}{n} \cdot n} = a$$

$a^{\frac{1}{2}}$ squared is a. $\qquad a^{\frac{1}{3}}$ cubed is a. $\qquad a^{\frac{1}{n}}$ to the n power is a.

$a^{\frac{1}{2}}$ is a square root of a. $\quad a^{\frac{1}{3}}$ is a cube root of a. $\quad a^{\frac{1}{n}}$ is an nth root of a.

$$a^{\frac{1}{2}} = \sqrt{a} \qquad a^{\frac{1}{3}} = \sqrt[3]{a} \qquad a^{\frac{1}{n}} = \sqrt[n]{a}$$

Now let us investigate the meaning of $a^{\frac{m}{n}}$.

$$a^{\frac{m}{n}} = a^{m \cdot \frac{1}{n}} (a^m)^{\frac{1}{n}} = \sqrt[n]{a^m} \qquad a^{\frac{m}{n}} = a^{\frac{1}{n} \cdot m} = \left(a^{\frac{1}{n}}\right)^m = (\sqrt[n]{a})^m$$

Therefore, $a^{\frac{m}{n}} = \sqrt[n]{a^m}$ or $(\sqrt[n]{a})^m$.

Example 1: Write $\sqrt[4]{a^3}$ in exponential form.
$$\sqrt[4]{a^3} = a^{\frac{3}{4}}$$

Example 2: Write $a^{\frac{2}{5}}$ in radical form.
$$a^{\frac{2}{5}} = \sqrt[5]{a^2}$$

Example 3: Find $\dfrac{a^{\frac{2}{3}}}{a^{\frac{1}{2}}}$.

$$\frac{a^{\frac{2}{3}}}{a^{\frac{1}{2}}} = a^{\frac{2}{3} - \frac{1}{2}} = a^{\frac{4}{6} - \frac{3}{6}} = a^{\frac{1}{6}} \text{ or } \sqrt[6]{a}$$

Write each expression in radical form.

1. $b^{\frac{3}{2}}$ $\sqrt{b^3}$

2. $3c^{\frac{1}{2}}$ $3\sqrt{c}$

3. $(3c)^{\frac{1}{2}}$ $\sqrt{3c}$

Write each expression in exponential form.

4. $\sqrt[3]{b^4}$ $b^{\frac{4}{3}}$

5. $\sqrt{4a^3}$ $(4a^3)^{\frac{1}{2}} = 2a^{\frac{3}{2}}$

6. $2 \cdot \sqrt[3]{b^2}$ $2b^{\frac{2}{3}}$

Perform the operation indicated. Answers should show positive exponents only.

7. $\left(a^3 b^{\frac{1}{4}}\right)^2$ $a^6 b^{\frac{1}{2}}$

8. $\dfrac{-8a^{\frac{3}{4}}}{2a^{\frac{1}{2}}}$ $-4a^{\frac{1}{4}}$

9. $\left(\dfrac{b^{\frac{1}{2}}}{b^{-\frac{2}{3}}}\right)^3$ $b^{\frac{7}{2}}$

10. $\sqrt{a^3} \cdot \sqrt{a}$ a^2

11. $\left(a^2 b^{-\frac{1}{3}}\right)^{-\frac{1}{2}}$ $\dfrac{b^{\frac{1}{6}}}{a}$

12. $-2a^{\frac{1}{3}} b^0 \left(5a^{\frac{1}{2}} b^{-\frac{2}{3}}\right)$ $\dfrac{-10a^{\frac{5}{6}}}{b^{\frac{2}{3}}}$

Algebra 1

Enrichment

Pythagorean Triples

Recall the Pythagorean theorem:
In a right triangle, the square of the length of the
hypotenuse is equal to the sum of the squares of the
lengths of the legs.

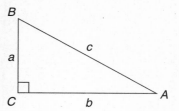

$a^2 + b^2 = c^2$
Note that c is the length of
the hypotenuse.

The integers 3, 4, and 5 satisfy the
Pythagorean theorem and can be the
lengths of the sides of a right triangle.

$$3^2 + 4^2 = 5^2$$
$$9 + 16 = 25$$
$$25 = 25$$

Furthermore, for any positive integer n,
the numbers $3n$, $4n$, and $5n$ satisfy the
Pythagorean theorem.

For $n = 2$: $6^2 + 8^2 = 10^2$
$$36 + 64 = 100$$
$$100 = 100$$

If three numbers satisfy the Pythagorean theorem, they are
called a **Pythagorean triple.** Here is an easy way to find other
Pythagorean triples.

The numbers a, b, and c are a Pythagorean triple if
$a = m^2 - n^2$, $b = 2mn$, and $c = m^2 + n^2$,
where m and n are relatively prime positive integers and $m > n$.

Example: Choose $m = 5$ and $n = 2$.

$a = m^2 - n^2$	$b = 2mn$	$c = m^2 + n^2$	**Check:** $20^2 + 21^2 = 29^2$
$= 5^2 - 2^2$	$= 2(5)(2)$	$= 5^2 + 2^2$	$400 + 441 = 841$
$= 25 - 4$	$= 20$	$= 25 + 4$	$841 = 841$
$= 21$		$= 29$	

Use the following values of m and n to find Pythagorean triples.

1. $m = 3$ and $n = 2$

2. $m = 4$ and $n = 1$

3. $m = 5$ and $n = 3$

4. $m = 6$ and $n = 5$

5. $m = 10$ and $n = 7$

6. $m = 8$ and $n = 5$

Algebra 1

NAME_____ DATE _____

Enrichment

Pythagorean Triples

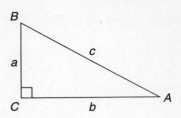

Recall the Pythagorean theorem:
In a right triangle, the square of the length of the hypotenuse is equal to the sum of the squares of the lengths of the legs.

$a^2 + b^2 = c^2$
Note that c is the length of the hypotenuse.

The integers 3, 4, and 5 satisfy the Pythagorean theorem and can be the lengths of the sides of a right triangle.

$$3^2 + 4^2 = 5^2$$
$$9 + 16 = 25$$
$$25 = 25$$

Furthermore, for any positive integer n, the numbers $3n$, $4n$, and $5n$ satisfy the Pythagorean theorem.

For $n = 2$: $6^2 + 8^2 = 10^2$
$$36 + 64 = 100$$
$$100 = 100$$

If three numbers satisfy the Pythagorean theorem, they are called a **Pythagorean triple.** Here is an easy way to find other Pythagorean triples.

The numbers a, b, and c are a Pythagorean triple if
$a = m^2 - n^2$, $b = 2mn$, and $c = m^2 + n^2$,
where m and n are relatively prime positive integers and $m > n$.

Example: Choose $m = 5$ and $n = 2$.

$a = m^2 - n^2$	$b = 2mn$	$c = m^2 + n^2$	**Check:** $20^2 + 21^2 = 29^2$
$= 5^2 - 2^2$	$= 2(5)(2)$	$= 5^2 + 2^2$	$400 + 441 = 841$
$= 25 - 4$	$= 20$	$= 25 + 4$	$841 = 841$
$= 21$		$= 29$	

Use the following values of m and n to find Pythagorean triples.

1. $m = 3$ and $n = 2$
12, 5, 13

2. $m = 4$ and $n = 1$
8, 15, 17

3. $m = 5$ and $n = 3$
30, 16, 34

4. $m = 6$ and $n = 5$
60, 11, 61

5. $m = 10$ and $n = 7$
140, 51, 149

6. $m = 8$ and $n = 5$
80, 39, 89

Algebra 1

13-4

Enrichment

Using Radical Equations

The circle with center C and radius r represents Earth. If your eye is at point E, the distance to the horizon is x, or the length of tangent segment ED. The segment drawn from C to D forms a right angle with ED. Thus, $\triangle EDC$ is a right triangle. Apply the Pythagorean theorem.

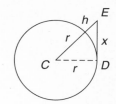

$$(\text{length of } CD)^2 + (\text{length of } ED)^2 = (\text{length of } EC)^2$$
$$r^2 + x^2 = (r + h)^2$$
$$x^2 = (r + h)^2 - r^2$$
$$x = \sqrt{(r + h)^2 - r^2}$$

1. Show that this equation is equivalent to $x = \sqrt{2r + h} \cdot \sqrt{h}$

If the distance h is very small compared to r, $\sqrt{2r + h}$ is close to $\sqrt{2r}$.
$$x \approx \sqrt{2r} \cdot \sqrt{h}$$
The radius of Earth is about 20,900,000 feet.

$\sqrt{2r} \approx \sqrt{2(20,900,000)} = \sqrt{41,800,000} \approx 6465$ feet. Thus, $x \approx 6465\sqrt{h}$.

If you are h feet above Earth, you are about $6465\sqrt{h}$ feet from the horizon. Since there are 5280 feet in one mile,

$$6465\sqrt{h} \text{ feet} = \frac{5465\sqrt{h}}{5280} \text{ miles} \approx 1.22\sqrt{h} \text{ miles}.$$

Thus, if you are h feet above Earth's surface, you can see $1.22\sqrt{h}$ miles in any direction.

2. How far can you see to the nearest mile if your eye is:
   a. 1454 feet above the ground (the height of the Sears Tower)?
   b. 30,000 feet above the ground (altitude for a commercial airliner)?
   c. $5\frac{1}{2}$ feet from the ground?

A strong wind can severely alter the effect of an actual temperature on the human body. For example, a temperature of 32°F is much more dangerous on a windy day than on a still day. Windchill is a temperature value assigned to a particular combination of wind speed and temperature. If w is the speed of the wind in miles per hour and t is the actual temperature in degrees Fahrenheit, then the approximate windchill temperature in °F is given by the formula

Windchill temperature $= 92.4 - \dfrac{(6.91\sqrt{w} + 10.45 - 0.477w)(91.4 - t)}{22.1}$.

This formula gives reasonably accurate results for the windchill temperature when $5 \leq w \leq 30$ and $-30 \leq t \leq 50$.

3. Find the windchill temperature to the nearest degree when the actual temperature is -15°F and the wind speed is
   a. 10 mi/h   **b.** 20 mi/h   **c.** 30 mi/h.

4. Find the windchill temperature to the nearest degree when the wind speed is 20 mi/h and the actual temperature is
   a. 30°F   **b.** 0°F   **c.** -30°F

Enrichment

Using Radical Equations

The circle with center C and radius r represents Earth. If your eye is at point E, the distance to the horizon is x, or the length of tangent segment ED. The segment drawn from C to D forms a right angle with ED. Thus, $\triangle EDC$ is a right triangle. Apply the Pythagorean theorem.

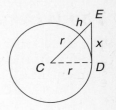

$$(\text{length of } CD)^2 + (\text{length of } ED)^2 = (\text{length of } EC)^2$$
$$r^2 + x^2 = (r + h)^2$$
$$x^2 = (r + h)^2 - r^2$$
$$x = \sqrt{(r + h)^2 - r^2}$$

1. Show that this equation is equivalent to $x = \sqrt{2r + h} \cdot \sqrt{h}$

$$\sqrt{(r + h)^2 - r^2} = \sqrt{r^2 + 2rh + h^2 - r^2} =$$
$$\sqrt{2rh + h^2} = \sqrt{h(2r + h)} = \sqrt{2r + h} \cdot \sqrt{h}$$

If the distance h is very small compared to r, $\sqrt{2r + h}$ is close to $\sqrt{2r}$.
$$x \approx \sqrt{2r} \cdot \sqrt{h}$$

The radius of Earth is about 20,900,000 feet.

$$\sqrt{2r} \approx \sqrt{2(20,900,000)} = \sqrt{41,800,000} \approx 6465 \text{ feet. Thus, } x \approx 6465\sqrt{h}.$$

If you are h feet above Earth, you are about $6465\sqrt{h}$ feet from the horizon. Since there are 5280 feet in one mile,

$$6465\sqrt{h} \text{ feet} = \frac{5465\sqrt{h}}{5280} \text{ miles} \approx 1.22\sqrt{h} \text{ miles}.$$

Thus, if you are h feet above Earth's surface, you can see $1.22\sqrt{h}$ miles in any direction.

2. How far can you see to the nearest mile if your eye is:
   a. 1454 feet above the ground (the height of the Sears Tower)? **about 47 miles**
   b. 30,000 feet above the ground (altitude for a commercial airliner)? **about 211 miles**
   c. $5\frac{1}{2}$ feet from the ground? **about 2.9 miles**

A strong wind can severely alter the effect of an actual temperature on the human body. For example, a temperature of 32°F is much more dangerous on a windy day than on a still day. Windchill is a temperature value assigned to a particular combination of wind speed and temperature. If w is the speed of the wind in miles per hour and t is the actual temperature in degrees Fahrenheit, then the approximate windchill temperature in °F is given by the formula

$$\text{Windchill temperature} = 92.4 - \frac{(6.91\sqrt{w} + 10.45 - 0.477w)(91.4 - t)}{22.1}.$$

This formula gives reasonably accurate results for the windchill temperature when $5 \le w \le 30$ and $-30 \le t \le 50$.

3. Find the windchill temperature to the nearest degree when the actual temperature is -15°F and the wind speed is
   a. 10 mi/h   b. 20 mi/h   c. 30 mi/h.   **-40°F -61°F -71°F**

4. Find the windchill temperature to the nearest degree when the wind speed is 20 mi/h and the actual temperature is
   a. 30°F   b. 0°F   c. -30°F   **4°F -39°F -82°F**

The Wheel of Theodorus

The Greek mathematicians were intrigued by
problems of representing different numbers and
expressions using geometric constructions.

Theodorus, a Greek philosopher who lived about 425
B.C., is said to have discovered a way to construct the
sequence $\sqrt{1}, \sqrt{2}, \sqrt{3}, \sqrt{4}, \cdots$.

The beginning of his construction is shown. You
start with an isosceles right triangle with sides
1 unit long.

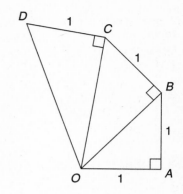

**Use the figure above. Write each length as a radical
expression in simplest form.**

1. line segment AO

2. line segment BO

3. line segment CO

4. line segment DO

5. Describe how each new triangle is added to the figure.

6. The length of the hypotenuse of the first triangle is $\sqrt{2}$. For
the second triangle, the length is $\sqrt{3}$. Write an expression
for the length of the hypotenuse of the nth triangle.

7. Show that the method of construction will always produce
the next number in the sequence. (*Hint:* Find an expression
for the hypotenuse of the $(n + 1)$th triangle.)

8. In the space below, construct a Wheel of Theodorus. Start
with a line segment 1 centimeter long. When does the Wheel
start to overlap?

Enrichment

The Wheel of Theodorus

The Greek mathematicians were intrigued by
problems of representing different numbers and
expressions using geometric constructions.

Theodorus, a Greek philosopher who lived about 425
B.C., is said to have discovered a way to construct the
sequence $\sqrt{1}$, $\sqrt{2}$, $\sqrt{3}$, $\sqrt{4}$, $\cdots$.

The beginning of his construction is shown. You
start with an isosceles right triangle with sides
1 unit long.

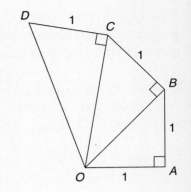

**Use the figure above. Write each length as a radical
expression in simplest form.**

1. line segment AO $\sqrt{1}$

2. line segment BO $\sqrt{2}$

3. line segment CO $\sqrt{3}$

4. line segment DO $\sqrt{4}$

5. Describe how each new triangle is added to the figure.
   **Draw a new side of length 1 at right angles to
   the last hypotenuse. Then draw the new hypotenuse.**

6. The length of the hypotenuse of the first triangle is $\sqrt{2}$. For
   the second triangle, the length is $\sqrt{3}$. Write an expression
   for the length of the hypotenuse of the nth triangle.
   $\sqrt{n+1}$

7. Show that the method of construction will always produce
   the next number in the sequence. (*Hint:* Find an expression
   for the hypotenuse of the $(n + 1)$th triangle.)
   $\sqrt{(\sqrt{n})^2 + (1)^2} = \sqrt{n+1}$

8. In the space below, construct a Wheel of Theodorus. Start
   with a line segment 1 centimeter long. When does the Wheel
   start to overlap?
   after length $\sqrt{18}$

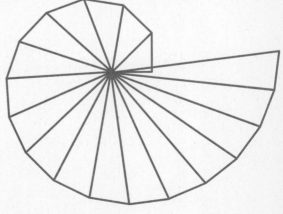

Enrichment

Graphing Circles by Completing Squares

One use for completing the square is to graph circles. The general equation for a circle with center at the origin and radius r is $x^2 + y^2 = r^2$. An equation represents a circle if it can be transformed into the sum of two squares.

$$x^2 - 6x + y^2 + 4y - 3 = 0$$
$$(x^2 - 6x + 9) + (y^2 + 4y + 4) = 0$$
$$(x^2 - 6x + 9) + (y^2 + 4y + 4) = 3 + 9 + 4$$
$$(x - 3)^2 + (y + 2)^2 = 4^2$$

Notice that the center of the circle is at the point $(3, -2)$.

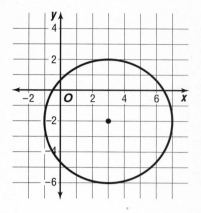

Transform each equation into the sum of two squares. Then graph the circle represented by the equation. Use the coordinate plane provided at the bottom of the page.

1. $x^2 - 14x + y^2 + 6y + 49 = 0$

2. $x^2 + y^2 - 8y - 9 = 0$

3. $x^2 + 10x + y^2 + 21 = 0$

4. $x^2 + y^2 + 10y + 16 = 0$

5. $x^2 - 30x + y^2 + 209 = 0$

6. $x^2 - 18x + y^2 - 12y + 116 = 0$

7. $x^2 + 30x + y^2 - 4y + 193 = 0$

8. $x^2 + 38x + y^2 - 12y + 393 = 0$

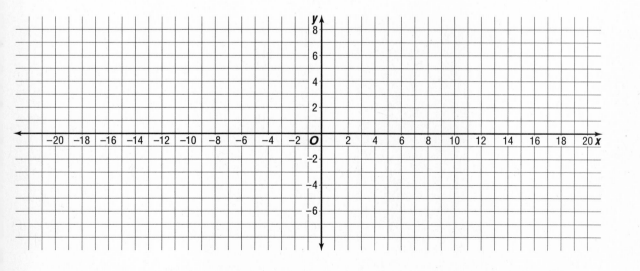

Algebra 1

Enrichment

Graphing Circles by Completing Squares

One use for completing the square is to graph circles. The general equation for a circle with center at the origin and radius r is $x^2 + y^2 = r^2$. An equation represents a circle if it can be transformed into the sum of two squares.

$$x^2 - 6x + y^2 + 4y - 3 = 0$$
$$(x^2 - 6x + \quad) + (y^2 + 4y + \quad) = 0$$
$$(x^2 - 6x + 9) + (y^2 + 4y + 4) = 3 + 9 + 4$$
$$(x - 3)^2 + (y + 2)^2 = 4^2$$

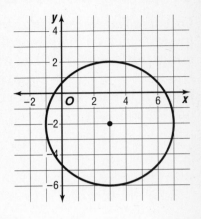

Notice that the center of the circle is at the point $(3, -2)$.

Transform each equation into the sum of two squares. Then graph the circle represented by the equation. Use the coordinate plane provided at the bottom of the page.

1. $x^2 - 14x + y^2 + 6y + 49 = 0$
   $(x - 7)^2 + (y + 3)^2 = 3^2$

2. $x^2 + y^2 - 8y - 9 = 0$
   $x^2 + (y - 4)^2 = 5^2$

3. $x^2 + 10x + y^2 + 21 = 0$
   $(x + 5)^2 + y^2 = 2^2$

4. $x^2 + y^2 + 10y + 16 = 0$
   $x^2 + (y + 5)^2 = 3^2$

5. $x^2 - 30x + y^2 + 209 = 0$
   $(x - 15)^2 + y^2 = 4^2$

6. $x^2 - 18x + y^2 - 12y + 116 = 0$
   $(x^2 - 9)^2 + (y - 6)^2 = 1^2$

7. $x^2 + 30x + y^2 - 4y + 193 = 0$
   $(x + 15)^2 + (y - 2)^2 = 6^2$

8. $x^2 + 38x + y^2 - 12y + 393 = 0$
   $(x + 19)^2 + (y - 6)^2 = 2^2$

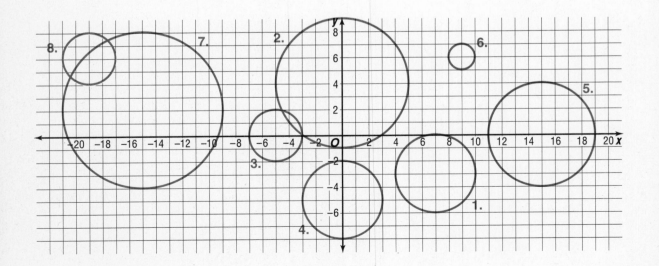